Preface

In the Far East, for over 1,000 years, soybeans have been used as one of the most important sources of protein and oil. But, since they have a hard texture, oriental peoples have been compelled to process the beans into various soy foods, all of which are digestible and palatable. Some of these processed foods are produced on a small scale in the home, and others are factory-produced and distributed over wide areas. Today, however, with increasing consumption in Japan of such Western foods as meat and dairy products, the popularity of soybean foods has leveled off.

But, because feed protein produces low yields of animal protein and because animal foods are expensive, soybeans deserve greater attention as a valuable source of food proteins. And, indeed, for more than ten years, defatted soybeans have been used in processed soy foods that simulate meat and other nonvegetable products.

These products are beginning to take root in the food markets of the United States and Japan. Furthermore, American consumers now display great interest in such traditional oriental soybean foods as tofu, soy sauce, and *tempeh*. In other words, people in the West are starting to realize not only the physiological and nutritional value of these foods, but their palatability and acceptability as well.

This book introduces soybeans as the basic material of a variety of traditional and modern foods found today mainly in Japanese markets and includes both village-type or homemade favorites as well as mass-produced foods, which have played a large role in popularizing soybeans. I shall be extremely pleased and honored if this book contributes to the readers' better understanding of soybean foods.

I should like to express my gratitude to Dr. W. J. Wolf of the Northern Regional Research Center of the United States Department of Agriculture and to Miss Yoshiko Kojima of the Tokyo office of the American Soybean Association for their kind and useful advice and suggestions. I should like to thank the Ishigame Co. Ltd., Takahashi Shōten Co.; Toyo Plant Co. Ltd.; the Takai Tofu & Soymilk Equipment Co.; Misuzu Tofu Co. Ltd.; the Kikkoman Corporation; the Nagata Brewing Machinery Co., Ltd.; and other companies and individuals for providing photographs and illustrations of their equipments and products. But the mention of the specific brand names of equipment and foodstuffs must not be interpreted as commercial endorsement on my part.

This book could never have been completed without the wonderful patience of Mr. Iwao Yoshizaki, president of Japan Publications, Inc.; and Ms. Yotsuko Watanabe, editor in the same firm; and Mr. Richard L. Gage, who translated my Japanese manuscript.

Finally, I should like to say that having an opportunity to work with Mrs. Asako Kishi, who was in charge of part II of the book and who cooperated with me as a specialist in connection with photographs and illustrations, was a source of great happiness.

In the light of the food shortage that is foreseen for the near future, the people of the world must devote cool thought to ensuring and distributing foodstuffs on a global basis. We must all do everything we can to save even one of those people who are threatened with death by starvation unless the food crisis is solved. This book will have fulfilled its purpose if in some way it helps by contributing to the replacement of expensive, low-yield meat with soybean proteins.

TOKUJI WATANABE

Nature's Miracle Protein

THE BOOK OF
SOYBEANS

By Tokuji Watanabe, D. Agr.
with Asako Kishi

Japan Publications, Inc.

Published by JAPAN PUBLICATIONS, INC., Tokyo and New York

Distributors:
UNITED STATES: *Kodansha International/USA, Ltd., through Harper & Row, Pub-
lishers, Inc., 10 East 53rd Street, New York, N. Y. 10022.* SOUTH AMERICA:
Harper & Row, Publishers, Inc., International Department. CANADA: *Fitzhenry &
Whiteside Ltd., 150 Lesmill Road, Don Mills, Ontario M3B 2T6.* MEXICO AND
CENTRAL AMERICA: *HARLA S. A. de C. V. Apartado 30–546, Mexico 4, D. F.*
BRITISH ISLES: *International Book Distributors Ltd., 66 Wood Lane End, Hemel
Hempstead, Herts HP2 4RG.* EUROPEAN CONTINENT: *Fleetbooks, S. A., c/o Feffer
and Simons (Nederland) B. V., Rijnkade 170, 1382 GT Weesp, The Netherlands.*
AUSTRALIA AND NEW ZEALAND: *Bookwise, 1 Jeanes Street, Beverley, South Australia
5009.* THE FAR EAST AND JAPAN: *Japan Publications Trading Co., Ltd., 1–2–1,
Sarugaku-cho, Chiyoda-ku, Tokyo 101.*

First edition: June 1984

LCCC No. 84–080644
ISBN 0–87040–513–6

Printed in Singapore

Contents

Part 2:   Cooking with Soybean Food Products

Part One

General Information

Introduction

Historical Background

According to Chinese written records, soybeans were cultivated as early as 2800 B.C. These documents give detailed information on cultivation, strains, harvesting, preservation, and use of soybeans together with those of such other major crops as wheat, barley, and millet. The place of origin is usually given as East Asia, which is not entirely definite. But it seems likely that primitive Chinese discovered that the beans of wild soy plants were edible and gradually improved them into a cultivated crop through strain selection.

Since they are easily grown and do not require highly fertile soil and since the beans themselves resist insect infestation and can be stored for extended times, soybeans have long been highly prized in China as a source of needed nutrients in time of famine. But, even in time of plenty, because of their high protein and oil content, soybeans have played a vital part in the Chinese diet. Ways of processing them into foods were imported together with the plants and their cultivation methods into Korea and Japan, where, as is well known, soy products have long been used and are still widely consumed.

Over the centuries in which soybean-foods have been eaten in East Asia, the need for protein in the diets of vegetarian Buddhist monks has stimulated the development of rich variety of processing and preparation methods. The many emigrant Chinese who now live in Southeastern Asia display the conservative nature of human attitudes toward food by continuing to produce and consume in their new countries the same kinds of soybean foods they and their forebears ate in China.

The agricultural manual *Qimin Yaoshu*, which dates from between 400 and 500 of the Christian Era and is considered the oldest agricultural treatise in existence, includes detailed farmer guidance and full accounts of how to process and use economically the precious agricultural products that are the result of farm labor. Of course various ways of eating soybeans are contained in this document.

Because soybeans have root nodules, the plant requires little nitrogen fertilizer since the *Rhizobium* bacteria in the nodules fix nitrogen from the air by converting it to nitrate. Furthermore, the amount of protein produced by soybeans per unit area is higher than that of any other crop.

The seed structure of soybeans is so hard that merely boiling or roasting them is insufficient to render them digestible. These very limitations have inspired people to process the beans in numerous ways to make them easy to digest, palatable, favorite foods.

Like the method for cultivating them, ways of eating soybeans were introduced into Japan from China; but, once accepted, soybean foods were modified to suit Japanese tastes and prepared in ways to harmonize especially well with rice, the Japanese dietary staple.

World Production and Use

Today, as in the past, China produces a large quantity of soybeans: though exact figures are unavailable, it is estimated that the annual Chinese production cannot have been less than 8 million tons in 1982 and 1983. Though at one time Japan produced a million tons annually, with imports from the United States increasing after World War II, the domestic crop was gradually reduced to reach the level of no more than 100 thousand tons. In recent times, however, with reductions in the rice harvest, the amount of soybeans grown has risen to the 200-thousand-ton level. Indonesia grows 600 thousand tons a year, and North and South Korea from 250 to 300 thousand tons each. The world's foremost producer, the United States raises 62 million tons annually. The Americans use the beans largely as an oil source. Brazil has an annual crop of 15 million tons and the amount is increasing sharply. In the past five years in Argentina crops have rapidly increased to reach the level of 3.5 million tons. The Soviet Union raises 500 thousand tons annually. The total world crop is over 90 million tons a year. Table 1 shows world production by nations.

Though nations like China, Japan, Korea, and Indonesia with long traditions of using soybeans for food still devote most of their crops to such purposes, other countries like the United States, Brazil, and Argentina, where soybean culture is a comparative innovation, use the largest part of their crops for oil and convert the defatted soybeans into animal feed. Large-scale animal husbandry demands constant, stable feed sources. Defatted soybean meals and fish meals meet these needs; but, recently, it has become apparent that the use of soybeans for this purpose is unsatisfactory from the feed-efficiency standpoint. Research is now being carried out on the conversion of soybeans to human food. For instance, in the animal-grazing nations, soybeans are employed in the production of products with the consistency and texture of meat that can be combined with animal meat in processed foods. Other nations, especially the developing countries, where protein supplies are insufficient are now studying the possibilities of raising soybeans, though they have never had such crops before, and of employing the harvests as food.

In addition to meeting its own needs, the United States exports vast amounts of soybeans. In 1982 it exported 2.0 million tons to West Germany, 5 million tons to Holland, 3.0 million tons to Spain, 840 thousand tons to France, 640 thousand tons to England, 900 thousand tons to Italy, 4.0 million tons to Japan, 460 thousand tons to Israel, 1.1 million tons to Taiwan, 590 thousand tons to Korea, 310 thousand tons to Canada, 290 thousand tons to Mexico, and 650 thousand tons to the Soviet Union. The United States also exports defatted soybean meals remain-

Table 1   World production of soybeans (1000t)

	1977	1978	1979	1980	1981	1982
United States	48,097	50,859	61,722	48,772	54,435	61,969
China	7,250	7,565	7,460	7,940	9,330	8,700
Brazil	9,541	10,060	15,153	15,200	12,800	14,600
Argentina	2,700	3,700	3,600	3,500	4,000	3,400
Soviet Union	545	634	467	525	450	480
Japan	111	190	192	174	212	226
Others	3,948	4,243	5,109	4,673	4,988	5,468
Total	72,192	77,251	93,703	80,784	86,215	94,843

Table 2   Price trends in dollars per ton for wheat,
soybeans, and corn

	Wheat	Soybeans	Corn
1970	65.40 (100.0)	109.96 (100.0)	59.45 (100.0)
1971	61.73 (94.3)	115.53 (105.2)	46.45 (78.1)
1972	92.59 (141.6)	141.92 (129.1)	56.89 (95.7)
1973	223.59 (341.9)	230.75 (209.9)	103.14 (173.5)
1974	173.61 (265.4)	274.84 (250.0)	140.94 (237.0)
1975	133.29 (203.8)	177.84 (161.7)	104.92 (176.5)
1976	97.19 (148.6)	251.51 (228.7)	94.68 (159.3)
1977	101.41 (155.1)	216.42 (196.8)	86.91 (146.2)
1978	130.53 (199.6)	246.92 (224.6)	89.37 (150.3)
1979	156.25 (238.9)	233.86 (212.7)	105.51 (177.5)
1980	169.57 (259.3)	274.47 (249.6)	141.33 (237.7)
1981	114.27 (174.7)	244.72 (222.6)	109.07 (183.5)

Note: Figures in parentheses are based on a value of one hundred
for the year 1970.

ing after its domestic-feed quotas are met: in 1982, 360 thousand tons to Canada, 740 thousand tons to West Germany, 1.0 million tons to Italy, and 49 thousand tons to Japan. The annual total export of defatted soybeans from the United States is 6.2 million tons.

Obviously various factors influence international soybean prices. In 1972 and 1973, abnormal weather and a rapid increase in animal-food consumption aggravated the supply-and-demand balance in feed, produced a world food crisis, and drove prices of American soybeans suddenly up. This was a blow to Japanese cattle raisers and to homemakers who felt the influence of bean prices on the tofu and other soybean products they included in their daily menus. Since then, prices have remained steady but high. The world demand for soybeans is unlikely to drop. Further, such direct or indirect influences as abnormal weather cannot be neglected. Thus the prices of soybeans are unlikely to decrease. Table 2 shows price trends in dollars per bushel for the past ten years for wheat, soybeans, and corn according to the Chicago market.

Nutritional Values

Nutritionally, soybean composition, which is different from those of other beans and grains, contains from 35 to 40 percent protein, from 15 to 20 percent oil, and from 20 to 25 percent sugar. Furthermore, soy proteins are nutritionally superior among vegetable proteins since they contain good supplies of essential amino acids, though they are slightly deficient in such sulfur-containing amino acids as methionine and cystine. Combining soybean foods with rice solves this problem. The methionine missing in soybeans is supplied by the rice; the lysine missing in rice is supplied by the soybeans. The fatty acids in soybeans are such unsaturated fats as oleic acid, linoleic acid, and linolenic acid. This means that soybean oils are useful in reducing heart ailments, which may be caused or aggravated by excessive intake of cholesterol from animal fat. The fatty acids represented by linoleic and linolenic acids have another nutritional effect. The presence of a large percentage of sucrose in soybeans further increases their nutritional value.

Though they lack starches, soybeans include such other carbohydrates as cellulose, hemicellulose, pectine, and phytic acid. Not only does cellulose promote good elimination, it and other indigestible dietary fibers have been shown to be instrumental in maintaining good physical condition and preventing rectal cancer.

In spite of its abundant nutritional contents, the soybean has, as has been said, a hard texture and is therefore difficult to digest. Some way had to be found to overcome this fault. And, over centuries, the Chinese discovered ways to do this and to take advantage of the excellence of these beans. The processing methods evolved for soybeans are as follows.

First is the production of soy milk by wet-milling the beans, boiling them, and finally removing indigestible elements. Second is boiling the beans after soaking them in water overnight and then introducing microorganisms to ferment them. In the first method, when the indigestible elements are removed in the form of what is called *okara*, or pulp, a highly digestible liquid—soy milk—remains. It may be used as a beverage or a basis for other foods. In the second process, microorganisms grown on the cooked soybeans result in mechanical and biochemical degradation of the beans' structure, which immensely improves their digestibility and also supplements the enzymes in the digestive tract.

Interestingly, the same processes that improve soybeans' digestibility enrich their palatability too. Soy milk is more palatable than soybeans themselves, and the texture and delicacy of its coagulated proteins have made bean curd—tofu— a favorite throughout the Orient. The microorganisms in fermented soy products produce characteristic flavors, and the amino acids in the same product stimulate the taste buds. Furthermore processing soy milk into tofu and cooked soybeans into miso (bean paste) disguises what characteristic odors may be present in the soy milk and cooked soybeans.

As has already been pointed out, soybeans—the meat of the fields, as they are often called—produce more proteins per land unit than any other grain or legume, as these statistics show: rice—25.6 kilograms of protein per 10 acres, wheat—21.1 kilograms, sweet potato—25.4 kilograms, and soybeans—48.9 kilograms. Pasture, which can be harvested several times yearly, produces 140 kilograms per ten acres; but since it cannot be eaten directly by human beings, its protein output is useful in the human diet only after it has been transformed into such foods as milk, butter, and meat by grazing animals. As a matter of fact, the proteins produced in milk, pork, chicken meat, and eggs per unit of land areas is greater than that of soybeans; but animals demand long periods of care and great quantities of concentrated feed. Furthermore their feed efficiency is very low. In terms of protein efficiency, if the protein in feed given to animals is taken to be 100, milk returns 30 percent, eggs 25 percent, and meat from 10 to 20 percent.

It is sensible to obtain high-protein food from animals by feeding them the grasses that human beings cannot eat. It is wasteful, however, to attempt to do the same thing by feeding animals such potentially valuable raw materials as grains, fish, and soybeans, as is done. Though these proteins could be better returned to human use, they are not always.

Between 1972 and 1976, of the 250 million tons of proteins produced annually in the world, 50 million tons were animal proteins. Of the remaining 200 million tons of vegetable proteins, 100 million tons was fed to animals as feed. Of the total amount of annually produced vegetable proteins oily nuts seeds and beans like soybeans, peanuts, cotton seeds, rape, and coconut, account for 39 million tons or 15.8 percent of the total. Of this, soybeans account for 60 percent, or 9.5 percent of total protein production. In other words, in the light of the limited amount of vegetable resources, the importance of soybeans is great. But, as has been pointed out, a large percentage of the world's soybean crop is fed to animals after the oil has been removed.

Storability

Perishables like milk, eggs, and meat, all of which have high water content, require processing—into such things as processed meats, sausage, butter, cheese, powdered milk, or dried eggs—if they are to be stored for long periods of time. This naturally raises the cost of these processed foods. In contrast, soybeans, which have a water content of no more than 13 percent, may be stored at low temperatures and low humidity for long periods without deterioration. In addition, they may be processed into storable foods on a regional basis, as is done in Japan and China.

Costs

The annual high protein yield of soybeans per land-area unit—greater than that of any other crops—naturally means that costs of the soybean foods are lower. The difference between costs of soybean proteins and animal proteins is even more striking when the prices of concentrated feeds needed for large-scale animal husbandry are taken into consideration. The processing of soybeans into food products naturally raises the cost, still it is at about the level of egg prices and much lower than the prices of other animal proteins. The cost of soybean food proteins will drop even more in the future when they are manufactured on a large scale. Assuming the unit price of proteins from unprocessed beans to be 1, we see that the figures for tofu are from 12 to 15, for dried-frozen tofu (*kōri-dōfu*) from 12 to 15, for *yuba* 40, for *kinako* (soybean powder) from 5 to 6, for *nattō* 10, for milk from 25 to 30, for eggs 10, for sliced ham 40 to 50, for pork from 40 to 50, for chicken from 20 to 25, for beef from 60 to 70, for mackerel 15, and for tuna from 20 to 25. In other words, soybean and soy-product proteins are clearly cheaper than all animal proteins except those found in eggs.

1. Characteristic Traits

Agronomic and Other Biological Characteristics

One of the legumes, soybeans (*Glycine Max* Merrill) have been cultivated in China, Japan, Korea, and other East Asian nations for centuries. In the nineteenth to twentieth centuries, they were introduced into the United States, Canada, Europe, and South America. Today, soybeans are raised in a wide range of places and climates. As has already been said, they have a greater protein production per unit of land area than any other crop food. In recent years, this output has been on the increase. Table 3 shows recent trends for soybean-protein output per ten ares in Japan and the United States.

Table 3 Trends in soybean production (unit kg per 10a)

	United States	Japan
1974	156	143
1975	194	145
1976	175	132
1977	205	140
1978	198	150
1979	216	147
1980	177	122
1981	204	142

In terms of photosynthesis, corn is a so-called C_4 plant; soybeans are C_3 plants. This means that the first photosynthetic products in corn are four carbon compounds (C_4) and the first ones in soybeans are three carbon compounds (C_3). C_4 compounds are readily converted to C_6 compounds (glucose) in the next phase. If genetic engineering can modify soybeans to enable them to use the C_4 dicarboxylic acid cycle, their crop output per unit of land measure will be greatly improved.

Soybean is a short-day plant. It will not bloom if the day is too long. But some varieties are not too sensitive to daylight. In Japan, there are two types, the summer type and the autumn type. The autumn type, which is altricial, has the characteristic of blooming when day time begins to become shorter, in the fall. No clear sensitivity to daylight is noticeable in the summer type, which is precocial. Summer-type soybeans are sown in the spring and harvested in June or July; autumn-type soybeans are sown in June and July and harvested in November and December.

Because of shorter growing period, the per-unit output of summer-type soybeans

Fig. 1   Soybean plant with flowers and beans.

is low; but they tend to have a high protein content: as much as 45 percent. Very precocial soybeans are raised in western Japan from the spring into the summer. Autumn-type soybeans, moving from precocial to altricial, are raised from the northern island of Hokkaido and southward. Because Japan is long north and south and has regionally varied climate, production of huge quantities of soybeans of uniform quality is difficult. But this geographic characteristic stimulates the people of each region to make good uses of the traits of local soybeans to produce distinctive local soybean foodstuffs.

Different climate and soil conditions in cultivation regions result in the wide variety of kinds of soybeans raised in Japan. For this reason, it is desirable to categorize and market varieties according to the kinds of foods in which they will be used: tofu, miso, soy sauce, and so on.

The United States is divided into nine belts for precocial and altricial soybean cultivation, and suitable varieties of plants grouped 0 to VIII are raised in each belt. Groups 0–II·correspond to the Japanese summer type, and groups VI–VIII to the Japanese autumn type. The most precocial varieties are raised in the north; and the farther south the belt, the more altricial the soybean crop. Some soybean plants form vines that grow along the ground very much like the wild *Glycine Soja* that is the source from which modern soybeans have been developed.

In terms of agronomical properties, the soybean plant (Fig. 1) may be described as follows. There is considerable variation in plant height among varieties. Though some are as high as an adult human, the usual height is about 50 centimeters. If the plant is too tall it is difficult to harvest, especially with combines. Furthermore, on tall plants the beans at the top and those at the bottom are likely to be in different stages of maturity; this too is undesirable. On the other hand, plants that are too low are difficult to harvest with combines, especially if the pods grow to the ground.

Dehiscence—the drying of the pod to eject the seed at maturation—is often a problem at harvesting, since beans cast on the ground in this way are lost to combines. To prevent this loss, strains that do not completely eject their beans are desirable.

Physical Properties

Exterior form: Most soybean seeds are spherical, but some are ovoid, long ovoid, or flattened spherical. They all become ovoid after soaking in water. Their surface is often smooth and glossy. The bean consists of the seed coat; the cotyledon, a primary part of the seed; and the hypocotyl, which is attached to the pod by means of the hilum. The hypocotyl, adjacent to the hilum, consists of the plumule and the radicle. Proportions of these parts are as follows: seed coat, from 6 to 8 percent; cotyledon, from 87 to 90 percent; and hypocotyl, from 2 to 2.5 percent.

Color: Most soybeans are yellow, though there is some variation in color: green, purplish black, and dark brown varieties exist. In the United States, all commercial beans are yellow; others are excluded by grading standards. But in all varieties the cotyledon is yellow. In black varieties, the color of the seed coat transfers to the cotyledon during cooking. Some varieties are speckled, for instance the variety that is green with black spots. In some varieties, the cotyledon as well as the seed coat is green.

Size: Beans range from large ones that weigh from 300 to 400 grams per 1,000 seeds (300–400 milligrams per seed) to small ones weighing no more than 120 grams per 1,000 seeds (120 milligrams per seed). Domestic Japanese soybeans are generally large, though small varieties are preferred for the production of *nattō*.

Microstructure: Microscopic examination shows that the cross section of a soybean seed coat consists of palisade cells of epidermis (*p ep*), hourglass cells (*s ep*),

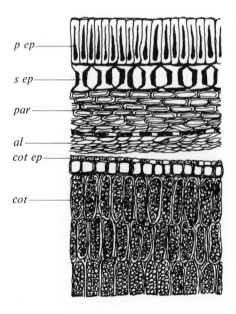

Fig. 2 Cross section of soybean seed-coat and cotyledon: *p ep*, palisade cells of epidermis, *s ep*, hourglass cells, *par*, parenchyma, *al*, aleurone cells, *com*, compressed cells of the endosperm, *cot ep*, cotyledon epidermis, and *cot*, aleurone cells of the cotyledon.

p ep
s ep
par
al
cot ep
cot

parenchyma (*par*), aleurone cells (*al*), and compressed cells of the endsperm (*com*). The cotyledon, separated by the epidermis from the seed coat, consists of cotyledon cells (Fig. 2). The cotyledon cell contains protein bodies (called aleurones) and oil in spherosomes or lipid bodies. As transmission electron microscopy reveals, the protein bodies are 2 μm to 20 μm in diameter; and the spherosomes are 0.2 μm to 0.5 μm.

Chemical Properties

Soybeans are rich in protein and oil and contain such carbohydrates as sugars and cellulose, as well as inorganic matter. In addition, they contain vitamins and various enzymes. The chemical composition of the bean and soybean foods is shown in Table 4.

Table 4   Chemical compositions of soybean foods (in 100 g)

	Moisture	Protein	Fat	Carbohydrate		Ash
				Soluble	Fiber	
	g	g	g	g	g	g
Tofu (regular)	86.8	6.8	5.0	0.8	0	0.6
Abura-agè	44.0	18.6	33.1	2.8	0.1	1.4
Kōri-dōfu	10.4	53.4	26.4	7.0	0.2	2.6
Yuba	8.1	50.2	33.4	5.3	0.2	2.8
Kinako	5.0	35.5	23.4	26.4	4.6	5.1
Soybean sprouts	88.3	5.4	2.2	2.6	0.8	0.7
Nattō	59.5	16.5*	10.0	9.8	2.3	1.9
Miso (dark yellow)	45.7	13.1*	5.5	19.1	2.0	14.6
Soy sauce (common)	69.5	7.5*	trace	7.1	0	15.9
Soybean (Japanese)	12.5	35.3	19.0	23.7	4.5	5.0

* Include low-molecular N-compounds. Protein$=N \times 5.71$

Climate and especially variety influence chemical composition. For instance, Japanese summer-type soybeans have a high protein content. Soybeans grown in the United States, cultivated as material for oil extraction, have high oil contents. Chinese and Japanese soybeans have high carbohydrate contents, which account for sweetness in miso and soy milk. It is important to note that the same variety of soybean can have different chemical compositions when grown in different soils and climates.

Cellulose is found mostly in the seed coat; hemicellulose and other polysaccharides constitute the cell wall. Starch, though present in the beans before they ripen, is almost entirely absent in mature beans.

Sucrose is the most plentiful sugar (from 6 to 7 percent) in soybeans, though other such oligosaccharides as stachyose (from 1 to 2 percent) and raffinose (5 to 6 percent) are present. Protein, which may account for as much as from 30 to 40 percent, is largely salt-soluble globulin and partly albumins.

The oil content, which may account for roughly 20 percent, consists largely of unsaturated fatty acids (80 percent) like oleic and linoleic acids.

The vitamin content of soybeans is varied: 0.5 milligrams of vitamin B_1 (more than the 0.4 milligrams in unpolished rice), other members of the B group (riboflavin, niacin, pantothenic acid), carotene, the precursor of vitamin A, and vitamin E. The ash (5 percent) in soybeans contains such essential minerals as potassium, phosphorus, sodium, calcium, and sulfur. Unlike most animal foods, which are acidic, soybeans are alkaline, though the significance of alkalinity in foods has not yet been established.

Soybeans contain some undesirable materials: for instance, trypsin inhibitors have the undesirable effect of preventing digestion and breakdown of proteins. But these substances are rendered almost inactive by the application of moist heat to soybeans. Other undesirable substances in soybeans are hemagglutinins, which cause clumping of red blood cells in test-tube experiments. But these too are unstable when submitted to heat treatment and are therefore of no concern in soybean food products. Soybeans further contain the flatus factors that cause gastrointestinal gas. Though they do no definite harm, they do inhibit the use of soybeans as food in United States. The substances involved in the flatus factors are largely oligosaccharides like raffinose, stachyose, and verbascose, most of which are broken down in the production of fermented products like miso and soy sauce.

Soybean oil contains lecithin, sterols, and dissolved chlorophyll. Lecithin and cephalin, both belonging to the phosphatide group, are present at a rate of about 2 percent together. Lecithin, which can be obtained from soybean oil, has excellent emulsifying characteristics and is used as an emulsifier in the production of chocolate and as a medicine. It is believed to prevent accumulation in the blood of cholesterol, a cause of disease. Sterols are compounds similar to vitamin D and hormones in chemical structure. Saponins, present in soybeans to the extent of 0.6 percent, form a soapy foam when mixed with water. It is noteworthy that saponins have recently been revealed to prevent the formation of peroxidized oil, which helps cause senility. In addition, isoflavon, and phytin are present in soybeans. Isoflavones, yellow substances accounting for the water-solubility of soybeans color, have been found to have the same effects as saponins. Soybeans are said to contain a goitrogenic substance that has an enlarging effect on goiters caused by iodine deficiency; but, as of yet, the substance has not been chemically identified. There is no problem in the region where seaweed is supplied to provide iodine.

Soybean Protein

Soybeans are closer in chemical composition to peanuts than to ordinary beans. First, soybeans contain from 30 to 40 percent protein compared with from 20 to 25 in other beans. Moreover, whereas other beans contain more than 50 percent starch, soybeans are almost completely lacking in this substances. In contrast with other beans, which usually contain less than 1 percent oil—except peanuts which contain 45 percent—soybeans contain roughly 20 percent.

Proteins in foods are indispensable to the growth of children and to the replacement of cells lost through aging and degeneration in adults. In both cases, balance of essential amino acids must be maintained. This means a necessary intake of animal proteins, since in general amino-acid balance is inferior in vegetable proteins. For instance, lysine is missing in proteins from wheat and tryptophane in corn proteins. For this reason, people whose diet centers on wheat or corn often suffer from protein deficiency. Soybeans and rice too fail to guarantee good amino-acid balance: soybeans are deficient in methionine and cystine, and rice in lysine. But extent of insufficiency is less than in the cases of corn and wheat. As has been said, combining rice and soybeans results in a balanced diet since the two kinds of food mutually make up for each other's amino-acid deficiency. Today when, in Japan and the West, protein intake from animal foods transcends a certain level, the proteins from soybeans have a nutritional effect nearly equal to that of animal proteins.

Furthermore, it has become clear that adults do not need as much of the sulfur-containing amino acids, cystine and methionine as was formerly thought.

Ninety percent of the proteins in ground soybeans is extracted in water. Addition of acid to the extract to bring the level to pH 4.5 precipitates most, but not all, of the proteins. Some remain dissolved in the supernatant, showing that there are several kinds of proteins in soybeans: some that are not water-soluble, some that are water-soluble and can be precipitated at pH 4.5, and some that are water-soluble and cannot be precipitated at pH 4.5. The ones that are soluble and precipitable, the major part of soybean protein, are mainly a mixture of two globulins called glycinin and β-conglycinin. The ones that are soluble but not precipable are albumins and globulins with molecular weights smaller than those of glycinin and β-conglycinin.

Soy milk is produced by wet milling the beans, adding water, boiling the slurry, and filtering it. The proteins in this milk, though denatured by heat, correspond roughly to the water-soluble proteins mentioned above. Addition of calcium salt or acid to soy milk produces a curd called tofu, which corresponds to glycinin and β-conglycinin. The protein that remains dissolved in the liquid (whey) corresponds to albumin and globulins, other than glycinin. Many of the new products now being produced from soybeans are made from soybean meal that has been defatted by means of hexane as the solvent. By adding water or alkaline solution to un-heated, defatted meal, the protein is almost completely dissolved. An extract is obtained by filtration to remove insolubles. Addition of acid precipitates glycinin and β-conglycinin. They are washed and dried to produce what is called isolated soybean protein, which is more than 90 percent pure. Care must be taken to prevent denaturation of the protein of defatted soybeans in the solvent-extraction process. During the process, use of alcohol or high temperature denatures the protein, decreases its solubility, and reduces the yield of isolated protein. When denaturation is prevented, the product is called undenatured, defatted soybeans. The water solubility of proteins in defatted soybeans (NSI, or Nitrogen Solubility Index) is measured by extracting solubles from a sample by means of forty times the sample's weight of water, filtering, determining the nitrogen in the extract, calculating the soluble nitrogen, and representing it as a percentage of the nitrogen in the original sample.

Proteins from undenatured, defatted soybean meal are highly water soluble, but their solubility in acid and alkali differs remarkably according to the pH value of the extract. Solubility increases as the extract moves from neutral to alkaline. Reduction of the pH by addition of acid reduces the amount of proteins dissolved (Fig. 3). Minimum protein solubility occurs when the extract pH value is about 4.5. This value is the isoelectric point of protein and corresponds to maximum protein precipitation from a water extract. Extraction of protein from soybean meal with calcium chloride has a minimum at 0.017N, corresponding to maximum precipitation concentration of protein from water extract, as in the case of acid. Though its extent of extraction is higher than that of acids (Fig. 4), calcium chloride is used in the manufacture of tofu. Since the process involved is hot extraction, proteins precipitate to a greater degree than is the case when cold-water extraction is used. Indeed, the extent of precipitation is almost as high as it is when acid is used. Magnesium chloride too is used. But sodium chloride produces a lower

Fig. 3 Protein (N) solubility of defatted soybean meal at different pH values.

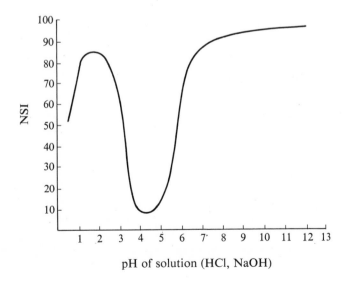

pH of solution (HCl, NaOH)

Fig. 4 Protein (N) solubility of defatted soybean meal at different concentrations of CaCl₂ (N).

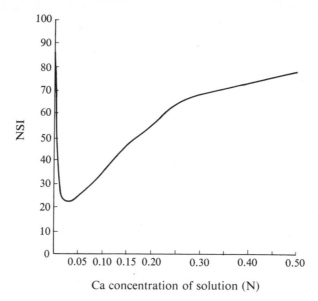

Ca concentration of solution (N)

degree of precipitation and a turbid supernatant. For tofu and isolated soybean protein, sodium chloride cannot be used.

Though heating of whole soybeans (as in the manufacture of *kinako*) or undenatured, defatted soybeans reduces protein water solubility, heating neither precipitates nor coagulates proteins dissolved in water. Nonetheless, some heat denaturation clearly takes place, since the solution is more turbid than it was before heat was applied. This suggests association of protein molecules. The viscosity of the protein increases. Proteins precipitated by means of acid from a heated solution have greater volume and greater water-retaining capacities than those precipitated from unheated solutions. To mold precipitated protein in boxes for tofu production, the protein must be heat-denatured and thus made more adhesive. Commonly, heating changes the physical, chemical, and biological properties of protein. The process is called heat denaturation and is usually understood to constitute structural changes of the protein molecule not accompanied by hydrolysis of the peptide linkage. The conditions under which heat is applied account for differences in the nature of these changes, and these differences are closely connected with the state or appearance of the food in which the protein is denatured.

Proteins that have not been heat-treated have a folded compact structure. Heating loosens this structure. As a result, proteolytic enzyme can come into contact with the interiors of the protein molecules and readily hydrolyze them. Heating of soybeans during food processing improves digestibility of the final products. This effect is even greater in soybean foods, which contain a substance that inhibits the action of the digestive enzyme trypsin. This substance is inactivated by heating. This discussion should demonstrate the reasonableness of heat-processing in the production of soybean foods and defatted soybeans for feed.

The protein in soybeans can be divided into three groups: globulins (the main fraction), whey protein, and insoluble protein. The globulins consist of several component. Ultracentrifugal analysis shows that they contain of 2S, 7S (conglycinin), 11S (glycinin) and 15S components (S is a unit of sedimentation speed per unit centrifugal force in an ultracentrifugation).

As has already been explained, soybean protein has a fairly well-balanced essential-amino-acid composition. Lysine is abundant; such sulfur-containing amino acids as methionine and cystine, however, are less plentiful than in animal proteins. Protein content in foods is usually calculated by multiplying Kjeldahl nitrogen by the nitrogen conversion factor. This factor differs, however, depending on the variety of protein, because protein nitrogen contents differ. In the United States, the accepted figure for soybean protein is 6.25, whereas in Japan it is 5.71. Protein content can differ by 10 percent depending on which figure is employed.

Properties of Soybeans as Food Material

Water Absorption

One of the traditional ways evolved to make soybeans more digestible for human food is to soak them in water overnight and then grind them. This process, called wet grinding, breaks soybean cells down easier and finer than dry grinding. After wet grinding, the slurry is heated and filtered to produce soy milk. This is the

Fig. 5 Relationship between time and temperature in soaking soybeans in water.

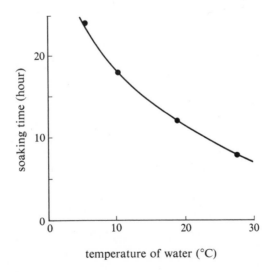

first step in making tofu. For the production of miso and *nattō*, soaked soybeans are steamed until soft. In both cases, the soaking time depends on the temperature of the soaking water. Soybeans must absorb about 1.2 times their own weight or volume of water. The higher the temperature of the soaking water, the higher the absorption rate, though too high a soaking temperature denatures soybean proteins. Fig. 5 shows rates of water absorption at different temperatures. The bean variety and conditions of postharvest handling and storage too affect the absorption rate. Found mixed among normal soybeans are some called hard beans, which retain almost their original weight and size in spite of soaking and absorb no water at all. Though many factors may be involved, the exact cause of these hard beans remains unclear. It is thought that extreme aridity after harvest is an important factor. Pricking a hole in the skins of hard beans restores their water-absorbing ability.

Some varieties, which absorb water at very high rates, soften by means of cooking without the preliminary overnight soaking. Used as ordinary vegetables instead of as dried beans, these soybeans (*hitashi-mame*) are distinguished from more popular varieties by the presence of starch.

Cooking Qualities

For miso and *nattō*, soybeans are soaked in water overnight and steamed until suitably and evenly softened. The amount of time required to produce this effect differs with bean variety. Carbohydrate content seems to have a correlation with softness. Beans that must be steamed a long time turn dark brown (according to the Maillard reaction). Since this is unsuitable in the manufacture of light-colored miso, soybeans that soften in a shorter steaming time are preferred. Equipment for high-temperature, short-time (HTST) heating is now used.

Beany Flavor

Cooking for several hours after soaking in water, as in the production of miso and *nattō*, results in a flavor (cooked taste) quite different from the beany flavor of raw soybeans. Soy milk, too, has its own distinctive flavor, as does tofu, which is produced by mixing calcium salt with soy milk. The tastes of soy milk and tofu differ from each other.

Traditionally the peoples of Asia have been fond of the tastes of soy milk and tofu, but have altered the tastes of raw or cooked soybeans by such processes as those used in producing miso and *nattō*. In general, however, all of these flavors have prevented soybeans from becoming popular as a food among Westerners, who usually dislike soy milk and the flavor of these soybean products.

Evidence indicates that, at least in the past, enzymatic oxidation of soybean oil produced the flavor of soy milk. When soybeans are crushed, lipoxygenase begins to react with oil, producing oxidized products with characteristic flavors. Preliminary or immediate heating after grinding prevents the generation of these flavors, which may account for the original beany flavor and for the distinctive taste of soy milk as well. Reports indicate that, at least to an extent, n-hexanol and n-hexanal account for the flavor of raw soybeans. Moreover, crushing of soybeans for oil extraction and the reaction of lipoxygenase should increase the amounts of n-hexanal. Because some of the taste-causing elements are not soluble in a nonpolar solvent and persist after the defatting process, defatted soybean meal too has a beany flavor, though some products derived from it do not. One such product is soybean-protein concentrate, in the production of which treatment with dilute acid or alcohol eliminates the substances causing the beany flavor, soluble carbohydrates, and other soluble compounds. As most proteins do not dissolve, the protein content of this concentrate is 70 percent on a dry basis. Still another such product is isolated soybean protein made by extracting solubles from defatted meal, precipitating protein with acid, and centrifuging to remove whey. The protein content of this isolate, which has a much less beany taste, is over 90 percent. Nonetheless, because some flavor-causing substances are tightly bound to the protein, the beany flavor is not completely eliminated.

Protein Water Solubility

As has been mentioned, from 80 to 90 percent of the protein (nitrogen $\times 6.25$) in finely ground soybeans dissolve in water, if the amount of water is sufficient. The same is true in the case of defatted soybean meal as long as no heat treatment or other processing that denatures the protein is used during solvent extraction. High-temperature drying after harvesting denatures soybean protein, which becomes insoluble in water. Storing soybeans in hot, humid places has the same effect on their proteins.

All these changes are expressed by a decrease in NSI, which is therefore an important means of evaluating not only defatted soybean meal, but also whole soybeans intended to be used as raw material in the production of such foods as tofu, miso, and soy sauce. Since it is desirable to heat soybean meal intended to be used as feed in order to inactivate its trypsin inhibitor and other substances, the NSI of such meal is usually below 30. The NSI of defatted soybean meal for use in the manufacture of soy sauce is from 30 to 60. For use in traditional foods, whole soybeans should have a high NSI (80–90) that should not be decreased by environmental factors.

Proteins in Soybean-food Processing

As has already been pointed out, heat treatment denatures soybean proteins, though the way the heat is applied results in different changes in protein properties. Heating—as in the case of steaming soaked whole beans—makes the protein in soybean tissues readily insoluble. Heating soy milk, on the other hand, does not render its protein insoluble. Heating coagulates the protein to a gel only when concentrations are 10 percent or higher, although, as is the case in the manufacture of tofu, even dilute protein solutions will coagulate to a gel if calcium or magnesium salt is added to them. Other traditional Japanese foods in which heat-induced changes play an important role are *yuba*, a film that forms on the surface of gently heated soy milk; dried-frozen tofu, which has a spongy texture; and deep-fried tofu (*abura-agè* and *gammodoki*). Apparently the response of soybean protein to environmental conditions accounts for the various characteristic textures of these foods. Elucidating the causes and effects of these changes would stimulate new development in soybean-protein products.

2. *Current Ways of Using and Processing Soybeans*

Throughout the World

As I have already said, soybeans were first cultivated in China, where, according to one theory, they have been employed as food for five thousand years. The Chinese have developed a wide variety of processed soybean foods that continue to play a part in their diet today. These foods may be broadly divided into two classes: those originating with soy milk and employing no microorganisms (tofu and processed versions of it); and those that employ microorganisms (miso, soy sauce, and fermented tofu).

Some kinds of tofu of various properties and forms either were not introduced into Japan at all or, if introduced, have never been extensively used. Generally, Chinese tofu may be firm with a dense, resilient structure or well dehydrated and some of them are about the thickness of heavy paper. In addition, the Chinese drink large quantities of soy milk, which is an important source of protein, and eat considerable amounts of *yuba*.

Since fermentation in miso and soy sauce continues after the action of the *kōji* as a consequence of the action of wild microorganisms different from the ones found in Japan, the Chinese products look and taste different from the ones produced in Japan. Furthermore they are eaten in many more ways, some of which are regional.

Soy oil pressed or extracted from beans is used in various kinds of cooking processes and may be converted to hydrogenated oil for use in margarine and shortening. Apparently still today, as in the past, meal remaining after the extraction of oil is used either as fertilizer or as animal feed.

In Japan, in addition to these traditional Chinese ways of preparing them, soybeans are used in *kinako* (roasted soy flour), dried-frozen tofu, and *nattō*, all of which are distinctively Japanese products. The cultivation of soybean sprouts was brought in from China, as was the method for pressing soybeans to extract oil. Since before World War II, however, when the system was introduced, the petroleum-solvent method has been employed to extract soy oil for use in cooking and in the preparation of margarine and shortenings. Though in Japan in the past, as in China, defatted soybeans remaining after oil extraction were used as fertilizer and animal feed, it was later learned that they could be employed in the production of soy sauce. Defatted soybeans are used for that purpose today. Nonetheless, the bulk of them is still employed in the production of animal feed, especially of concentrated feed for chickens and pigs. In addition, defatted soybeans are employed in the production of miso, tofu (especially *abura-agè*), and amino acid mixtures. Recently, either as they are or after protein concentration, they have been used widely in the manufacture of processed meat and fish products. Though they were formerly used in its production, sodium glutamate is now made by fermentation requiring no soybeans.

As has been mentioned, Japan depends on import for a large percentage of its soybeans. Since they have a high fat content, beans from the United States are used in this country as a source of oil. For this use alone, Japan annually imports more than 3 million tons of soybeans. For tofu and deep-fried tofu products, 450 thousand tons of domestic and imported soybeans are used; for miso, 170 thousand tons; for *nattō*, 80 thousand tons; for dried-frozen tofu, 30 thousand tons; and for other purposes, several thousand tons. In the production of soy sauce, 200 thousand tons of defatted soybeans are employed; in the production of amino acid mixtures, several tons of thousands. In addition, since defatted beans are used in part in the production of miso and tofu, on a whole-bean basis, the total amount of soybeans used for food annually in this country is nearly 1 million tons.

The Indonesians, as well as the Chinese, Japanese, and Koreans, traditionally eat soybean foods, especially *tempeh* and Chinese-type soybean foods.

Of the 62 million tons of soybeans grown in the United States in 1982, 40 million went into the production of oil. The bulk of the remainder was exported to such countries as Holland, West Germany, Spain, and Japan. And only a small part was domestically used in whole-bean form for foods. More than 80 percent of the 32 million tons of defatted soybeans remaining after oil production was used domestically. The remainder was exported to such nations as Holland, West Germany, Poland, and Italy. Though the largest part of the domestically used defatted beans went into animal feed, some of it—either as is or with protein concentration—was employed in the productions of processed meats. An additional amount was processed for use as food for the people of developing nations. The quantities so used are usually from 100 to 200 thousand tons, and it is noteworthy that these quantities have increased remarkably in the past decades.

It has frequently been emphasized in the Food and Agriculture Organization of the United Nations and UNICEF that production and food use of soybeans as one of the most important protein resources in the world should be promoted not only in oriental countries, but also in other countries all over the world. This is applicable, not only to the developing nations, but also to the industrialized nations, as is indicated by the current trend in the United States to reevaluate soybeans, formerly valued as nothing but a source of oil and animal feed, for their importance in relation to quantity, quality, and cost of protein. Such reevaluation is a stimulating shift in the direction of the use of soybeans for food production. As has already been explained, from the standpoints of efficiency and resources, it is much wiser to use soybeans as food for human beings instead of converting them into animal products. This is especially true of the developing nations, where introduction of animal husbandry for food is not easy. It is quite natural that in Africa, and Central, and South America soybean production is on the upswing.

Of course, when sufficient soybeans are produced to play an important role in the diets of these nations, making them palatable and attractive presents some problems. From various trials in the past several decades, several methods have been evolved. One is to increase protein content and nutritional value by adding soybeans in traditional local diets. This sometimes takes the form of additions of soy flour to wheat flour used in the preparations of food. But this method frequently results in alterations of taste and appearance of such foods and reduces their appeal. Another method is to employ soybeans or products made from them in replacement for traditional foods. This cannot always be satisfactorily done, but in Japan and China meatlike products have long been made from tofu and other soybean products. For instance, *yuba* layered, pressed, heated, and caused to cohere is cut and flavored to resemble meat. The word *Gammodoki* (balls made by mixing tofu with other slivered ingredients, forming the mixture into balls, and deep frying them) means chicken-meat analogue in Japanese. Furthermore, in the United States a baconlike product is made from defatted soy flour. In other words, the use of soy and soy products as substitutes for other foods is not farfetched. The third method is to eat foods made directly from soybeans with no attempts to simulate other foods. One promising field in this connection is beverages, which as the spread of cola drinks proves, can quickly become international. Soy milk, long a traditional drink with the Chinese, could be an easy way for other people to take advantage of the value of soy protein, if the problem of the soy-milk flavor can be solved.

In any event, no matter how much the volume of soybean production for food use increases in the world, unless people consume soy products, this growth will be less meaningful than it could be. An important hint in finding ways to make soy products palatable to other peoples is the current popularity of such foods as tofu and soy sauce in the United States. It is of the greatest interest to discover the causes. Do the Americans eat these foods out of concern for nutrition and health? Are they more interested in the economical value of soy protein? Do they discover good ways to cook and eat these foods?

Although international interest in soy as a source of protein in the human diet had been on the increase in the past decade, at present, soybeans are still more often thought of as sources of oil or animal feed or even as cash crops for export to other nations. It is pressingly important to urge producing nations to concentrate on soybeans as food and to help them achieve this goal by adapting soy products to local preferences.

Traditional Ways of Using and Processing

Fermented and nonfermented soy products, the two traditional oriental kinds, are both results of the wisdom of the people of old. Furthermore, both are distinctively flavored, easier to digest, and lacking in the characteristic soybean flavor. Table 4 on page 22 shows names and chemical components of these foods. Later, I shall explain the ways these foods are produced today. At this point I shall mention briefly the old-fashioned ways of making them.

Nonfermented Foods

For the sake of convenience, these may be classified as follows:

1. Roasted soy flour (*kinako*)
2. Fresh soy purée or slurry (*go*)
3. Soy milk
4. *Yuba* or film that forms on the surface of heated soy milk (usually sold in dried form)
5. Tofu or bean curd
6. Processed tofu
7. Soybean sprouts

Heat is essential to the production of all soybean foodstuffs since it inactivates harmful trypsin inhibitors and hemagglutinins. Furthermore, heating changes the three-dimensional structure of protein in ways that characterize the texture of various soybean foods and make it easily attacked by enzymes and thus more readily digested. Though heat is not needed in the raising of soybean sprouts, they must be cooked to make them better foods. The second essential process in the production of nonfermented soybean foodstuffs is a breakdown of the hard texture of soybeans to improve their digestibility.

According to recent Japanese data, rates of digestion and absorption of protein, fats, and carbohydrates in human beings are as follows: 95 for proteins and 97 for fats and carbohydrates in tofu, deep-fat-fried tofu, frozen-and-dried tofu, *yuba*, and soy milk; 91 for proteins, 91 for fats, and 97 for carbohydrates in cooked soybeans and *nattō*; and 78 for proteins, 87 for fats, and 97 for carbohydrates in *kinako*.

1. Roasted soy flour (kinako)

There are two grinding processes for soybeans: wet grinding and dry grinding. Since they contain about 20 percent oil, raw soybeans are difficult to grind. Toasting them before grinding results in a fragrant powdered product known as *kinako*. Sometimes the beans are coarsely ground, and the husks are removed before final grinding.

2. *Fresh soy purée or slurry* (go)

In wet grinding, the beans are soaked in water first; more water is added during the grinding process. In the past this work was done in stone mortars; today emery-coated grinders or impact-steel grinders and sometimes home-blenders are used. Heating this wet-ground product eliminates the beany flavor. This product, called *go*, is added to miso soup, though the practice has now gone out of popular use.

3. *Soy milk*

Soy milk is obtained by filtering *go*. Long a widely drunk beverage in China, soy milk has recently been marketed in Japan as well. It is more attractive to drink than *go* since the indigestible and insoluble materials have been strained out. *Yuba* and tofu are made from soy milk.

4. *Yuba*

Yuba is made by gently heating soy milk till a skin forms on the surface. This skin is carefully lifted off and dried for use in a variety of ways.

5. *Tofu*

There are several kinds of tofu, as shall be explained in detail later. All of them, however, are produced by adding calcium or magnesium salts to soy milk to coagulate it. The resulting curd, which contains protein and oil, is lightly flavored and of a pleasing, smooth texture. Differences in conditions and in the coagulating agent cause differences in texture of tofu from nation to nation.

6. *Processed tofu*

In Japan, the most popularly used processed tofu products—all of which, formerly made in the home, are now mostly factory prepared—are deep-fried tofu pouches (*abura-agè*), deep-fried tofu burgers (*gammodoki*), and deep-fried tofu cutlets (*nama-agè* or *atsu-agè*).

With its high water content, tofu does not keep well. Though they last longer than the fresh product, deep-fried tofu products too are perishable. But one tofu product—dried-frozen tofu (*kōri-dōfu*)—keeps excellently for long periods. In the past this product was made by exposing fresh tofu to winter-night cold till it froze, allowing it to thaw and dry the following day, and repeating this process till a dry spongelike substance resulted. Today this is done with refrigeration equipment, not just in winter, but at any season.

7. *Bean sprouts*

Addition of suitable degrees of moisture and heat to soybeans causes them to germinate and produce bean spouts, which, rich in vitamin C, are eaten like ordinary vegetables and play a nutritional role very different from that of usual soybean products. The germinating decreases protein content.

Fermented Foods

The three most outstanding fermented soybean products are miso and soy sauce, invented in China, and *nattō*, which originated in Japan. All of them are the result of the metabolic or fermenting actions of microorganisms abundant in the locations of the foods' origins. Consequently, though all three are made of soybeans, miso and soy sauce, in which *kōji* plays an important role, differ markedly from *nattō*, in which the fermenting element is a bacteria called *Bacillus nattō*.

The *kōji* for miso and soy-sauce production is made from steamed rice, roasted wheat, and soybeans, and serves the same fermenting purpose as the *kōji* used in sakè brewing or the malt used in beer brewing. After the *kōji* has been combined with the other ingredients, salt is added to inhibit other bacterial action; and the mixture is kept warm for fermentation. The enzymes produced within the *kōji* break down the starch in rice and the protein in soybeans. This chemical decomposition proceeds rapidly in the case of soy sauce because of the presence of large amounts of water, and the enzymes convert starch into sugar and proteins into dissolved amino acids. Since less water is present, in the preparation of miso, chemical reaction is less rapid; and much of the breakdown stops in mid-course. Commercially available spores of pure-cultured *Asp. oryzae*, the mold used in the preparation of *kōji*, are now widely employed for this process because they make possible development of the *kōji* mold before other bacteria have a chance to grow. Distinctive aromas and texture are sometimes created in miso and soy sauce by the invasion of wild yeast or lactic-acid bacteria. In the past, these microorganisms entered the mixtures fortuitously from the surroundings. Today, however, they are often cultured pure and artificially introduced.

To make *nattō*, steamed soybeans are inoculated with *Bacillus nattō*. The old-fashioned way of doing this was to wrap the beans, while still hot, in rice straw, where the wild bacteria grow. The bundles were then stored in warm places for from thirty to forty hours to allow the bacteria to grow on the surfaces of the beans. If allowed to stand too long, however, the bacteria themselves generate so much ammonia that their own further growth becomes impossible. No salt is used in the preparation of *nattō*. It is interesting to note that *Bacillus nattō* is a variety of *Bacillus subtilis*, which is little used in food production. Today *Bacillus nattō* is pure-cultured, and wooden boxes or plastic forms have taken the place of the old straw wrappings for fermentation.

The use of pure-cultured microorganisms in the manufacture of fermented foods prevents contamination by other microorganisms, ensures standardization of flavor quality, and simplifies production processes.

Other kinds of fermented soybean foods are made and eaten in other parts of the Orient. For example, the Chinese make a product called *sufu* by cultivating *Mucor* (a kind of mold) in tofu. The resulting mold-tofu is pickled in liquor of miso or in unrefined soy sauce and kept warm. In Indonesia, a food called *tempeh* is made by steaming soybeans, wrapping them in banana skins, and allowing them to ferment for one day or more. Originally, the fermentation relied on the *Rhizopus* mold in the banana skins. These microorganisms are now pure-cultured for this purpose.

New Soybean Food Products

Though the possibility of new uses in the human diet for soybeans was investigated in Germany and the United States during World War II, the movement never got very far. Later, however, using soybeans as additives and in this way taking advantage of the functional characteristics of soybean protein have been studied further; and practical applications resulted: (1) addition of soy flour or proteins extracted from it to bread ingredients to prevent retrogradation of starches, (2) addition of soybean flour to sausages to promote dispersion of fats, (3) addition of soy flour to doughnuts to prevent absorption of oil during frying. Some of these practices have persisted to the present.

In general, research on the use of soybeans in the human diet has concentrated on the combination of isolated proteins from defatted soybeans with other basic ingredients because Western nations where such studies are carried out regard soybeans primarily as a source of oil and are seeking ways to employ the defatted soybeans that remain when oil has been extracted. At present, the bulk of these defatted soybeans is used for animal feed. Several things should be said about this approach. First, as has already been pointed out, conversion of such material into feed is a much less effective way to make use of soybeans than the ancient oriental ways of employing whole beans in food preparation. Obviously it is preferable to feed animals materials that are little suited to human consumption. There are places where animal husbandry is impractical. For such zones, studies should be made on devising foods made from defatted soybeans and tailored to suit the tastes and needs of the local population. But this is a problem to be solved in the future. More pressing at the present is converting to effective uses the defatted soybeans that developed nations now feed to animals.

Secondly, it must be realized that soybean proteins are much cheaper to produce than animal proteins. Furthermore, they can be produced in much greater quantities for a given unit of land and a given span of time.

Thirdly, as is widely known, excess consumption of such animal proteins as those found in meat, milk, and eggs produces an excess of animal fats (largely saturated fatty acids) that can lead to cardiac ailments. Combination of these proteins with soybean proteins reduces intake of fats. Indeed, it is possible to convert totally to soybean proteins and to eliminate animal fats entirely from the diet. This is one of the reasons why people in the West are steadily showing greater interest in soybean proteins.

The following two points deserve serious consideration in making food products of defatted soybeans.

1. Elimination of their characteristic odor.
2. Increasing their protein percentage and allowing protein to function as fully as possible.

Since whole soybeans are their original source, defatted soybeans are rich in proteins. But the percentage of proteins in them can be increased by eliminating either the sugars or other soluble compounds or by removing such insolubles as fiber. To prevent the solution and loss of proteins when sugars and other soluble compounds are removed, soybean meal is often washed thoroughly with dilute acid or alcohol. After being separated from the acid or alcohol extract, the meal can be dried to produce what is called soy-protein concentrate. Insoluble fibers are removed from dilute alkali or water extracts of soy meal, which are then spray-dried to produce a kind of soy-protein concentrate. Adding acid to bring the pH value to 4.5 precipitates the protein, which can then be separated from the whey to produce soy-protein isolate. Protein concentrate, including defatted soybean meal, can be further processed to produce spun or textured proteins. Applications of these various soybean-protein products are explained later.

3. Tofu and Other Nonfermented Soybean Food Products

Tofu

Cotton, or Regular, Tofu

To make tofu, the proteins and fats in soybeans are extracted in hot water. Calcium sulfate, the coagulating agent, is added to this liquid. The coagulum is transferred to forms (usually box-shape) to set (Fig. 6). In addition to a high water content, tofu is rich in proteins and fats. Because it is easily digested and assimilated and because of its soft, smooth texture and bland flavor, it is very popular in Japan.

After being thoroughly washed, 10 kilograms of soybeans are allowed to stand overnight in more than 10 times their own volume of water. When they have fully absorbed water, the soybeans will have increased in

Fig. 7 Cotton tofu.

Fig. 6 Flow sheet of regular tofu production.

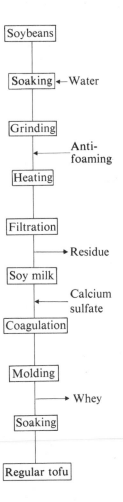

Soybeans

Soaking ← Water

Grinding

← Anti-foaming

Heating

Filtration

→ Residue

Soy milk

← Calcium sulfate

Coagulation

Molding

→ Whey

Soaking

Regular tofu

weight to from 22 to 23 kilograms. In summer, this requires from 7 to 8 hours; in winter, 15 hours or more. The soaked beans are then ground. Traditionally this is done in a stone mortar, though today emery-coated grinders (Fig. 8) are used. Water is gradually added throughout the grinding process. This grinding may be easily accomplished, but the coarseness of the mortar or grinder must be carefully regulated since, if the ground meal is too fine, in the the filtering stage, husks and other indigestible materials will pass through to become dispersed in the soy milk.

One hundred kilograms of water are added for every 10 kilograms of beans. Finally, after an antifoaming agent has been added, the slurry is transferred to a pot for heating. When a steam pot is used, the amount of water added must be reduced because condensation of steam increases moisture to some extent. When the

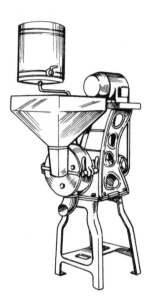

Fig. 8 Grinder for soaked soybeans (horizontal type).

Fig. 9 Continuous filter for soy-milk preparation.

Fig. 10 Small-scale soy-milk processing plant.

mixture reaches the boiling point, it must be stirred constantly to disperse the antifoaming agent—mixture of fat and calcium hydroxide, silcon resin, or mono-glyceride of fatty acids—evenly. In about 5 minutes, the raw smell of the soy mixture will have been lost; and there will be no further possibility of foaming. The mixture must next be filtered either in cloth or nylon bags. Pressure is applied either manually or hydraulically. Fig. 9 shows continuous filter and Fig. 10 is a typical soy-milk plant.

Before the soy milk extracted and filtered in this way has a chance to cool too much the coagulating agent (calcium sulfate or $CaSO_4 \cdot 2H_2O$) is added. This is done at a temperature of between 70°C and 80°C. Calcium sulfate, which will not dissolve in water, is stirred into water before being added and must be stirred during the addition to prevent its sedimenting. About 200 or 300 grams of calcium sulfate are needed for 10 kilograms of soybeans, though individual manufacturers may vary the amounts. The calcium sulfate may be dumped into the soy milk all at once while the liquid is being violently stirred and then allowed to settle quietly, or it may be added a little at a time. The method varies with locality and maker.

A thin wooden board (*kai*) is used to break up the coagulated white mass and stimulate separation of the liquid, which corresponds to the whey produced in

Fig. 11 Molding box for regular tofu.

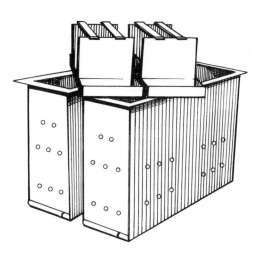

cheese manufacture. A bamboo colander is used to separate curd from whey, and the latter is dipped out with a wooden ladle (*bōzu*). The curds are then transformed to cloth-lined slitted wooden or perforated aluminium box forms (Fig. 11) The cloth lining is folded over on top of the curds. A bamboo mat is placed on top of this, and finally a weight is added to press the curds and remove additional whey, which drains out through the slits or holes in the box forms.

After a predetermined length of time, the weight and bamboo mat are removed. The cloth is unfolded, and the box mold is set, bottom down, into a vat of water. The liquid entering the molds from the bottoms forces the tofu up and free. Finally the cloth is gently removed. The still warm tofu is cut into the required sizes and slipped into a vat of cold water for the quickest possible cooling before being sold, usually in rectangular blocks weighing about 300 grams (500 in some regions) each. Because the weave of the cotton wrapper is imprinted on its surface, this kind of tofu is called cotton tofu. It is also known as regular tofu.

There is much regional variation in the manufacture of tofu. For example, in the Kanto area, where Tokyo is located, the box molds are narrow but deep; whereas, in the Kansai (Osaka, Kyoto, Kobe) region, they are shallow and square. Ratio of beans to water and consequently density of the resulting soy milk is not fixed. When the soy milk is highly concentrated, the whole milk in the vat coagulates, producing a smooth, soft tofu. When the density is low, on the other hand, coagulation is less thorough, the whey separates out, and the tofu tends to be slightly tough and coarse. When the temperature at which coagulation takes place is too high, the process advances too fast, the curds are too fine, and the resulting product is not only low in yield but tough in texture. When the temperature is too low, however, coagulation is incomplete; and the tofu is frail and lacks body. In this case too, yield is low. If the coagulating agent is present in excess quantity, the tofu is tough; and yield is low. If it is insufficient, the whey is inadequately clear; and the tofu lacks some of its characteristic features.

In the past, a substance called *nigari*, the main component of which is magnesium chloride, and not calcium sulfate, was the coagulating agent for tofu production. *Nigari* was obtained in the process whereby salt was obtained from seawater. Though it is said to taste good, tofu from *nigari* is too fine. Its yield is lower, and it tends to be tough. Calcium chloride too was used as a coagulating agent. But, since it produces a tofu very much like the kind obtained with *nigari*, it is not used alone now, though it sometimes supplements calcium sulfate.

Ten kilograms of soybeans will yield from forty to fifty kilograms of regular tofu. Differences in conditions and methods of production account for the variation in yield. Wooden vessels are widely used since they prevent undesirable rapid cooling of the tofu. But, inevitably, wooden surfaces become damaged with pits and cracks where lingering amounts of soy milk and coagulating agent become breeding grounds for microorganisms that, finding their way into the fresh batches of tofu, shorten their storability by increasing the danger of spoilage. To prevent this, wooden vessels are sterilized by means of heat; and the whole process must be protected from dust and dirt—especially from the dust rising from stored soybeans. Official regulations now require makers to employ metal vessels only. In any event, the utmost care must be exercised throughout the manufacturing process.

Regular tofu is frequently grilled over charcoal or, today, gas burners until its surfaces are toasted. This is done to produce a tofu that is firm enough not to fall apart when cooked for considerable lengths of time as is necessary in sukiyaki or in a favorite Japanese variety dish called *oden* if maximum flavor is to be absorbed from the stock. To firm its texture still more, toasted tofu (*yaki-dōfu*; Fig. 12) is given an extra pressing before grilling to extract more moisture.

The residue remaining after soy milk has been produced is called *okara* or *unohana* (Fig. 13). Though it formerly appeared on many Japanese tables seasoned and cooked with vegetables, today it is most often fed to animals. As the number of

Fig. 12 *Yaki-dōfu.*

Fig. 13 Okara.

animals raised in urban and suburban areas decreases, however, tofu manufacturers are finding it harder to dispose of residue. Statistics vary according to the way soy milk is prepared, but in general the residue contains about 20 percent vegetable protein on a dry basis.

In the past, Japan was self-sufficient in supply of soybeans for tofu manufacture. But in recent times, as crops have grown smaller, the Japanese people have come to rely on China and especially the United States for soybeans. Some beans are suitable for tofu production and some are not. In general, it can be said that beans with very high protein content produce very large yields of superior tofu. It is difficult to say that beans with comparatively low protein content are unsuitable for this purpose. The important thing for beans seems to be minimum yield fluctuation, no matter whether the coagulating agent is used in somewhat larger or smaller quantities. The amounts of phosphorus contained and protein components in the beans seem to affect the issue.

Tofu can be made from defatted beans, though the product is of inferior taste. To compensate for this, defatted beans are sometimes mixed with whole beans. Because they need neither an overnight soaking in water nor grinding, defatted beans are more convenient and increase the amount of tofu just before the production.

Silken Tofu (*Kinugoshi*) and Soft Tofu

Finer textured silken tofu is made from a soy milk produced from a slurry in which the amount of water is only five or six times the weight of the beans. This is heated and filtered just as in the case of regular tofu, but the tofu is set in box forms that have neither slits nor perforations (Fig. 14). In the case of direct heating, the high

Fig. 14 Molding box for silken tofu.

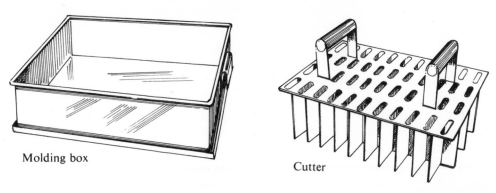

Molding box   Cutter

Fig. 15 Silken tofu.

Fig. 16 Flow sheet for silken-tofu production.

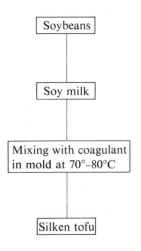

concentration of the soy milk makes necessary careful stirring during cooking to prevent scorching. During the steaming process, too, care is needed to regulate the temperature for, if it is too high, some of the proteins in the soybeans will become insoluble, lowering the protein-concentration of the soy milk. When the soy milk is at a temperature of 70°C, the suspension of calcium sulfate is added. The mixture is stirred and then poured into mold boxes. The amount of calcium sulfate is from 0.5 to 0.6 percent of the volume of soy milk. As has been said, silken-tofu form boxes lack the slits or perforations that are necessary for regular-tofu boxes to allow the whey to escape. The one hole in the bottom of each box is plugged from the outside. A single metal sheet is inserted in the bottom of each box; the soy milk and coagulating-agent mixture is poured on top of this. A lid is put on this, and the mixture is allowed to stand for from twenty to thirty minutes to gel (Fig. 16). Care is taken not to let the temperature drop. The denser the soy milk, the firmer the tofu. If the temperature is too high, the mixture will coagulate unevenly; and the whey will separate. If it is too low, coagulation will be insufficient; and the tofu will be too soft. If the coagulating agent is used in too great an amount, separation of whey and irregular coagulation will occur. If it is used in too small a quantity, coagulation will be insufficient; and the tofu will be too soft. When calcium chloride or magnesium chloride is used in place of calcium sulfate, unless the mixture is blended evenly and quickly, gelling will not take place; and whey will separate. Calcium sulfate dissolves in water only in small quantities. It is believed that the action of the dissolved part is responsible for gradual coagulation.

When the soy milk has coagulated, it is loosened from the box form by running a knife around the edges. The stopper is removed from the hole in the form bottom and the whole thing, bottom side down, is gently lowered into a vat of cool water. Bottom board and tofu are pushed out of the mold together, and the tofu is allowed to cool in the water before being delivered to customers or dealers.

The smooth texture of this kind of tofu plus the absence of the cloth marking imprinted by the lining fabric on regular tofu have resulted in the name silken tofu. In fact, no silk of any kind is employed in its manufacture.

In recent years glucono-delta-lactone (GDL) which dissolves readily and which, when heated in solution, breaks down into gluconic acid, has been widely used to make silken tofu. When a water solution of GDL is blended with soy milk heated to a temperature of from 70°C to 90°C, gluconic acid is formed and reacts with the soy milk to cause coagulation. Since the formation of gluconic acid is slow, the process of coagulation results in gelling, as is true in the case of calcium sulfate, which does not dissove in water readily.

At present silken tofu made with GDL is too bland in flavor in comparison with that made with calcium sulfate. Furthermore it lacks cohesion and consequently breaks easily. To compensate for these drawback, GDL is sometimes used in combination with calcium sulfate. Nonetheless, GDL alone has its advantages. The high temperature of the soy milk needed for coagulating with GDL reduces chances of error. Furthermore, product quality is invariable. Water solutions of GDL must be used soon after preparation. If allowed to stand, the production of gluconic acid proceeds; and the solution becomes useless as a coagulating agent for silken tofu. The accepted content of GDL is 0.3 percent of the soy milk. More than this results in a sour taste.

Yield of silken tofu is from four to five times the weight of soybeans used. The greater the amount of soy milk extracted, the higher the yield. If the milk is low in density, the tofu produced from it will be too soft. Since more water is used for regular tofu and since the milk from which it is made is less dense, loss in press residue (*okara*) is smaller than is the case in the production of silken tofu. On the other hand, the need to eliminate whey in the case of regular tofu increases loss.

In texture somewhere between regular and silken tofu, the product known as soft tofu is the result of efforts to duplicate the fine texture of silken tofu while giving the product somewhat more body. To prepare the soy milk for this kind of tofu a weight of water from seven to eight times that of the weight of beans is used. The coagulating agent may be calcium sulfate, GDL, or the two used in combination. The coagulating takes place in a vat and results in a gel about the texture of that in silken tofu. This is then ladled into the kind of box form used for regular tofu, covered with bamboo-mat lids, and weighted to eliminate whey. The soft tofu made in this way is widely eaten in Tokyo and in the Tohoku district (northeastern part of the island of Honshu). Sometimes this kind of tofu is made by lining a flat box with cloth, spreading a vinyl film on top of this, and pouring soy milk into the box for coagulation. When coagulation is complete, the film alone is pulled out. The curd is then weighted and finished as is done in the production of regular tofu. Still another method is to allow coagulation to take place in silken-tofu box forms and then to invert these over regular-tofu boxes so that the tofu is transferred from the former into the latter. It is then weighted and finished.

Packaged Tofu

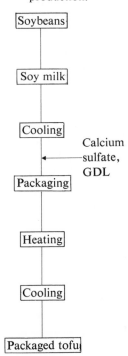

Fig. 17 Flow sheet for packaged-tofu production.

This sanitary product is produced by cooling soy milk, mixing a coagulant (calcium sulfate, GDL, or the two in combination) with it, injecting it into polypropylene or polyethylene boxes, sealing the boxes, and heating them and their contents in a water bath till the milk coagulates as silken tofu does. The weight of water for milk preparation should be from 5 to 6 times that of the soybeans. Cooling should be done quickly—plate coolers are used in plants with modern equipment—to limit chances for invasion and reproduction of micro-organisms. As a general rule, the sealed containers should be heated to 90°C for from 40 to 60 minutes, though adjustments must be made depending on the sizes of the containers and the time it takes for the heat to penetrate the contents (Fig. 17).

When coagulation is complete, the containers are cooled in water before being stored in refrigerators for later delivery. Since the tofu never comes in contact with human hands after the milk has been injected into the containers, this product is highly sanitary. Furthermore, it stores fairly well, being safe to keep in a refrigerator for from 4 to 5 days. Relatively easy to transport, it is produced in vast quantities for consumption in various

Fig. 18   Packaged tofu.

parts of the country. Some plants can produce from 50 to 100 thousand packs of this kind of tofu daily. Most of their product is sold from refrigerated supermarket showcases. Each pack contains from 200 to 300 grams and is shaped like a block of regular tofu. But to meet the needs of today's smaller families, convenient packs of less than 200 grams are now being marketed.

This packaging in which the kind of tofu is sold can be clearly labeled. Furthermore supplements of such vitamins as B_1 are not lost in immersion as is the case with both regular and silken tofu.

New Equipment

I have already mentioned the equipment used in small-scale factories. In factories where tofu is mass produced, labor-saving devices are employed. Steel impact grinders are avoided since they pulverize bean hulls too fine. Various ways of heating the soy slurry are available. In one system, the slurry moves along a horizontal screw conveyor through a chamber where steam is injected into it. Presses and centrifuges perform the filtering process. Ordinary centrifuges are only partly continuous in operation. More continuous and therefore more convenient for large plants is the screw decanter, the horizontal axis of which rotates to separate soy milk and residue within the machine in one continuous action. A deaerator is required to remove the air the screw decanter introduces into the soy milk.

Though delayed until recently, in the past few years, automation for labor reduction in the stage of making tofu from soy milk has begun developing rapidly. Perfectly continuous processing has not yet been attained, but coagulation for regular tofu is done in large batches; and curd is transferred by conveyor to the

Fig. 19 Large-scale process for tofu and *abura-agè* production.

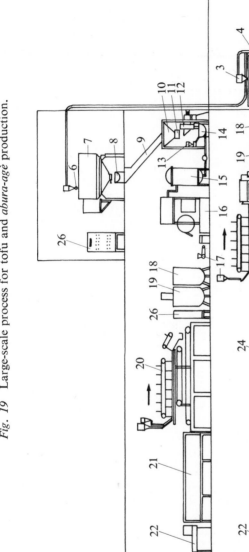

1—Boiler
2—Soybean pit and air conveyor
3—Cyclone
4—Silo
5—Weight measure
6—Soybean divider
7—Soybean tank
8—Washer and conveyor
9—Shooter for soaked soybeans
10—Hopper
11—Weight measure
12—Grinder
13—Antifoam measure
14—Slurry tank and pump
15—Cooker
16—Filter
17—Rotary feeder for discharging residue
18—Soy milk tank
19—Coagulant tank
20—Continuous tofu molder
21—Continuous tofu cooler
22—Tofu packer
23—Continuous tofu molder
24—Continuous deep fryer
25—Conveyor for packed products
26—Electric controler

molds. After this transferal process, weights are applied continuously to moving molds to remove whey. Devices for other aspects of the process are being used (Fig. 19). The process for mass production of silken tofu is much simpler than that for regular tofu. The soy milk is coagulated at once in a large vat into which are lowered metal plates assembled to cut tofu into the proper sizes and shapes. These are then transferred to vats of water for cooling prior to shipment.

Plate coolers are used to cool soy milk for packaged tofu. After the coagulating agent (calcium sulfate or GDL) has been added, the soy milk is pumped into containers by means of automatic devices that measure the right amount into each of the forms moving along a conveyor. When calcium sulfate is the coagulating agent, the mixture must be stirred since this substance does not dissolve readily. The mixture should not be kept at room temperature. The vinyl-film lids are automatically fitted in place and heat sealed. The packs are then carried by conveyor to the hot-water vats for heating. Conveyors then carry the packs to cold-water baths, where they are cooled to room temperature and finally to refrigerators for storage at above 0°C (Fig. 20).

Aseptic packed tofu is made by heating the mixture of sterilized soy milk and coagulant. The soy milk is heated to 130°C for a few seconds preliminarily to kill microorganisms and then cooled. The coagulants such as calcium sulfate and gluconodelta-lactone too are treated with Milipore filter to remove microorganisms. The mixture is then packed in presterilized plastic containers and sealed and heated. At room temperature it will keep without spoiling for about three months.

Fig. 20 Continuous process for packaged-tofu production.

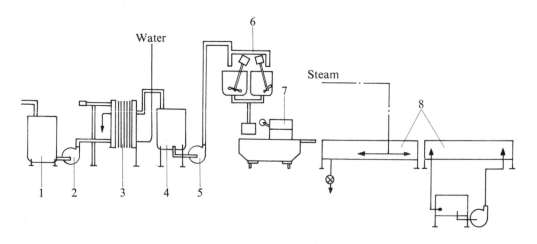

1—Receiving tank for soy milk	5—Sanitary pump
2—Sanitary pump	6—Mixing tank
3—Plate cooler for soy milk	7—Packaging machine
4—Storage tank	8—Boiling and cooling apparatus

Though at present, to protect small tofu makers, its production in Japan is largely limited, aseptic-packed tofu is manufactured for export and special uses.

Eating Tofu: The two most popular ways of serving tofu in Japan are chilled and seasoned with soy sauce and condiments (the dish is called *hiya-yakko*) in summer and heated in hot water and eaten with soy sauce and seasonings (the dish is called *yu-dōfu*) in winter. More often it is added to miso soup and used in Chinese dishes, especially one prepared with chili peppers and ground meat and called *maabo-dōfu* in Japanese. Tofu must be stored at above 0°C, for freezing alters its texture.

Deep-fried Tofu

In Japan, one-third of all the soybeans used in the production of tofu and its derived products are employed in deep-fried tofu of several kinds. Since their water content is low and since they have been thoroughly heated in the frying process, these foods keep longer without spoiling and are easy to transport. Large plants produce them on a big scale and distribute them throughout a wide area. Since freezing does not greatly alter their texture, as it does alter that of tofu, deep-fried tofu products are sometimes shipped frozen.

The most popular of these foods is *abura-agè* (Fig. 21), or deep-fried tofu pouches. They require thin tofu, which can either be specially made or produced by cutting ordinary tofu in thin slices horizontally, which are then pressed to remove some moisture and finally deep-fried in two stages. In the first stage, called

Fig. 21   Abura-agè.

Fig. 22 Continuous deep-frier for *abura-agè* production.

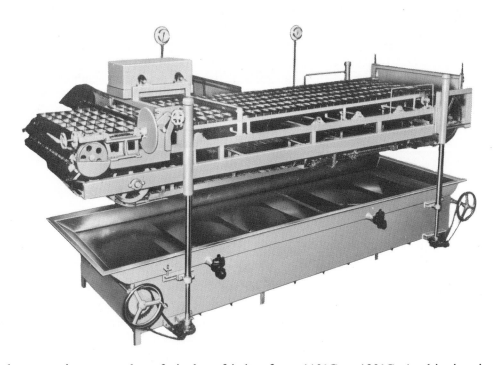

the expansion stage, the tofu is deep-fried at from 110°C to 120°C. At this time it expands greatly. In the second stage, called the fixing stage, the tofu is fried at temperature of from 180°C to 200°C. This removes moisture from the surface and fixes the shape. After frying, the tofu is about three times greater in area than it originally was. At present, tofu is fried by being immersed in hot oil in moving metal trays (Fig. 22).

In the past, when refining techniques were not as good as they are now, the oil—generally either soy or rapeseed oil—used in frying gave deep-fried tofu pouches a dark brown color. Today, however, because of the use of refined oil, they are a light gold. Both control of the frying temperatures and the production conditions under which the tofu itself is made are important in ensuring that the pouches will expand fully. If the soy milk is heated and coagulated at too high a temperature or for too long a time, curd proteins will bind to each other, limiting expansion during frying. To prevent this, in the process of tofu making, cold water is added to the mash after heating or to the coagulating soy milk to lower the temperature quickly. Addition of cold water also effectively retains air in the curd and may play a role in expansion.

In the first stage of frying (110°C–120°C), steam evaporating from the tofu causes it to expand and lighten. Consequently, the tofu floats in the oil; and its upper surface is exposed to the air. The undersurface, however, remains in the hot oil with the result that upper and under surfaces expand at different rates, causing the upper surface to curve inward. Forcing the upper tofu surface to remain immersed in the oil corrects this tendency. The second stage of frying (180°C) quickly dries the surface of the tofu and fixes its shape.

Deep-fried tofu is cut into thin strips for addition to miso soup or to be cooked together with seaweeds, vegetables, and seasonings. Though crisp on the outside, fried tofu remains soft on the inside. This makes it possible to slit the tofu pieces lengthwise to form bags or pouches, which, when filled with rice prepared for sushi and such other ingredients as *shiitake* mushrooms or vegetables, become a favorite dish called *inari-zushi*. Commercial manufacturers of large quantities of *inari-zushi* use air injectors to separate the layers to produce bags from deep-fried tofu. This is a great labor-saving device.

Nama-agè (Fig. 23), or *atsu-agè* (deep-fried cutlets), second to *abura-agè* in popularity among the deep-fried tofu products are thick tofu cutlets, pressed to remove some moisture and fried at a temperature of from 180°C to 200°C. Light brown in color, the tofu does not expand in frying; therefore, the element of expansion does not need to be taken into consideration in their production. Though available in various sizes and shapes, they are always thicker than deep-fried tofu pouches. They are generally simmered with other ingredients and with seasonings before being eaten.

Fig. 23   Nama-agè.

To make *gammodoki* (Fig. 24), or deep-fried tofu burgers, tofu is crumbled and drained in cloth bags. It is then combiined with various other ingredients in a kneader (Fig. 25) and formed into round patties or balls before being deep fried. When the added ingredient is a ground yam called *yamaimo*, the burgers expand more during frying. In addition, *yamaimo* acts as a binding agent. Frying is done in two stages, as in the case of deep-fried tofu pouches.

Fig. 24   Gammodoki.

Fig. 25   Tofu kneader for
gammodoki production.

Ingredients that may be added to tofu used for these burgers include julienne-cut carrot or burdock root, julienne-cut kelp, and sesame seeds. *Gammodoki*, the name of which is said to mean "analogous to poultry flesh," has a firmer texture than fresh tofu or *nama-agè*. They too are frequently cooked with seasonings and vegetables.

A fried tofu product made on the island of Shikoku and called *usu-agè* or *kara-agè* is made by deep frying very thin, firm tofu in two stages. The tofu expands to sizes much larger than ordinary *abura-agè*. Using in miso soup, *usu-agè* is very fragile; and the oil used in frying it tends to deteriorate. Mashed tofu paste may be used as a material in this product.

Dried-frozen Tofu (*Kōri-dōfu*)

Tofu is frozen, pressed, stored at a temperature below 0°C, thawed, and pressed again to further decrease moisture, and finally dried to make *kōri-dōfu*. Fresh tofu is difficult to press. Heating to dry it causes reduction in volume, casehardening, toughening, and a brown color. But freezing and storing it at a temperature below 0°C changes the texture of the tofu, which becomes spongelike. Extracting water from it then is easy, and it can be thoroughly dried (Fig. 27).

The natural way is to employ winter cold to do the freezing and sunlight to do the drying. In Japan a number of food products are made in this way. Most famous is an agar jelly called *kanten*. In crude form, this gel is frozen, thawed, and dried to give a more refined dried product. A kind of vermicelli called *harusame* is made by freezing, thawing, and drying the starch noodle of the mung bean. Similar processes are used with glutinous-rice cake and devils-tongue (*Konnyaku tuber*) gel (*konnyaku*, composed of glucomannan).

Originally, dried-frozon tofu resulted from letting ordinary tofu freeze at night in winter and thaw the next day. As this process was repeated over and over, the water content of the tofu drained off and diminished. In the deliberate production of dried-frozen tofu, a somewhat firm tofu is used. When the dried-frozen product has been rehydrated in hot water, it has a spongelike texture. This character is completely different from that of the original tofu. Though a dried form of tofu, dried-frozen tofu is now considered a separate food.

Though in the past, dried-frozen tofu was made in central and to an extent northern Japan as well as in the mountains of the western region, it is now popular

Fig. 26   *Kōri-dōfu*.

only in the western area alone. Characteristically, regions in which this product was made by natural means have cold, dry winters; abundant crops of soybeans; and good-quality water.

Fig. 27 Flow sheet for dried-frozen tofu (*kōri-dōfu*) production.

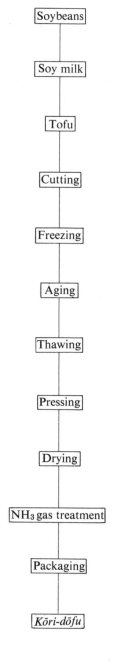

Today, virtually all the dried-frozen tofu made in Japan is produced by means of artificial freezing equipment and stored in refrigerators. Since it keeps and travels relatively well, this tofu product is manufactured in large quantities in big plants. Indeed, few small manufacturers remain in operation.

To make dried-frozen tofu, carefully selected soybeans are washed and, after standing in water overnight, ground with water in emery-coated or steel-impact grinders. After an anti-foaming agent has been added, the mixture is thoroughly heated by means of steam from a boiler. The batch is then filtered to give soy milk. The weight of water is over 10 times that of the soybeans. The concentration of the soy milk is almost the same as for regular tofu.

Since dried-frozen tofu is manufactured on a large scale, continuous equipment systems including cookers, centrifuges, molds, and drying devices are utilized.

When the soy milk is at a temperature of about 70°C, a calcium chloride solution is added to it and mixed thoroughly. The batch is allowed to coagulate. Separated whey is carefully removed, and the curd is broken by vigorous stirring till very fine. Lacking the water-holding powers of ordinary tofu, this curd produces a firm, uniform boxed tofu with a water content of less than 85 percent, in comparison with the 88 percent of regular tofu.

Removed from the forms, the tofu is immersed in flowing water, which cools it, prevents spoilage, and removes excess calcium chloride. After standing overnight or less in this water, it is cut into pieces of established dimensions (for instance 8×6×2 centimeters with a weight of 90 grams) and frozen, often by means of air-blast quick freezing till it reaches a temperature of about minus 10°C in from 1 to 2 hours. Small-scale operations may use ordinary freezers to do this job. Though quick freezing produces a desirably fine texture, if it is too rapid, the curd becomes insufficiently spongy. This results in inadequate water extraction and drying and lowers the quality of the product. In large plants, air-blast freezing is carried out continuously on conveyors. Once it has been frozen, the tofu is stored at temperatures of from minus 1°C to minus 3°C for a standard length of 3 weeks. Conversion of the tofu into a spongelike substance continues during this storage period. And, if the aging temperature is too low, the process will be hindered with the result that the final product will be less than satisfactory. On the other hand, if the temperature is too high, the curd will become too spongy; and the dried product or rehydrated product will be coarse and tough. Artificially frozen tofu of this kind is finer in texture than tofu frozen by the natural elements. Further, using artificial means, it is desirable to accelerate freezing at first by increasing the blast velocity to produce fine textured outer surfaces and then to decelerate it later by lowering that velocity to produce the kind of coarser inner layer necessary for efficient drying.

If the temperature drops too low, the product is of low quality, because all of the water in the tofu freezes, halting the process of protein denaturation, which is the cause of the spongy texture of this material. In large factories, after quick freezing, the tofu is packed in well-ventilated boxes and stored in a refrigerator where the temperatures mentioned above are maintained. Protein denaturation continues at these temperatures for about three weeks, but the aging period can be shortened by raising and lowering the temperature. For example, in natural production, when treated out of doors, the tofu thaws during the warm part of the day and freezes again at night; and the aging period is about two weeks. Ventilated boxes are employed since it is desirable for the tofu temperature to equalize with that of the refrigerator as quickly as possible. Showering water on its surface effectively raises the temperature of the tofu.

After the refrigeration period, flowing water is used to thaw the frozen tofu. In more primitive plants, the tofu is submerged in tubs into which water is constantly poured till it overflows. In large plants, however, the tofu is regularly aligned on broad, slow-moving, screen-belt conveyors and showered with water from above. Equipment of this kind makes possible continuous thawing.

Next it is necessary to apply pressure or use some device to force water out of the spongy thawed tofu. In older plants, this is done by putting the tofu into perforated containers and applying a hand-turned press. In some factories, the tofu is put in perforated baskets and centrifuged to remove water. Rubber rollers are used to squeeze water from frozen tofu thawed on continuous screen-belt conveyors.

Heat is then used to dry the spongelike tofu. But care must be taken not to apply high temperatures suddenly. If the heat is too great, evaporation from within cannot keep up with evaporation at the surface; and water remains in the tofu, making further drying extremely difficult. Sudden application of high temperatures causes contraction and cracking. On the other hand, if the drying temperature is too low, degradation can occur. In small plants, fixed amounts of tofu are dried at a time, though in larger factories, use of conveyors makes possible continuous drying of indefinite quantities.

To enable the finished product to swell and soften during the rehydration processes and cooking, it is temporarily exposed to ammonia gas introduced into the air of the sealed chamber where the dried tofu is being treated. The ammonia gas is retained in the openings of the spongy tofu but is driven out in cooking and therefore poses no health problems. But this does not mean that the ammonia-gas method is free of difficulties. First it is troublesome to carry out. Second it gives the product a distinctive odor. In addition, during shipping and storage it results in what is called the browning reaction; and, with the passing of time, the ammonia can dissipate, thus depriving the tofu of its desired swelling abilities in cooking. To solve this problems, recently another method has been developed and in large part put into practice. In this new system, phosphate and carbonate solutions are introduced at the thawing stage and allowed to penetrate into the thawed tofu. Drying is then performed after water has been partly removed.

A piece of tofu originally weighing 90 grams produces a piece of dried-frozen tofu weighing 20 grams and 7 by 7 by 1.8 centimeters. These pieces are usually packed from 5 to 10 to a package. Because it is desirable that all pieces in a package be equal in size and shape, some trimming is often needed. From 45 to 50 kilograms of dried-frozen tofu are produceable from 100 kilograms of soybeans. Matter that is insoluble during extraction with hot water remains for use as cattle feed. Substances remaining uncoagulated by calcium salts are removed as whey.

Because the production scale of dried-frozen tofu is fairly large in comparison with that of fresh tofu, factories making it are usually equipped for active sludge

Fig. 28 Process for large-scale dried-frozen tofu (*kōri-dōfu*) production.

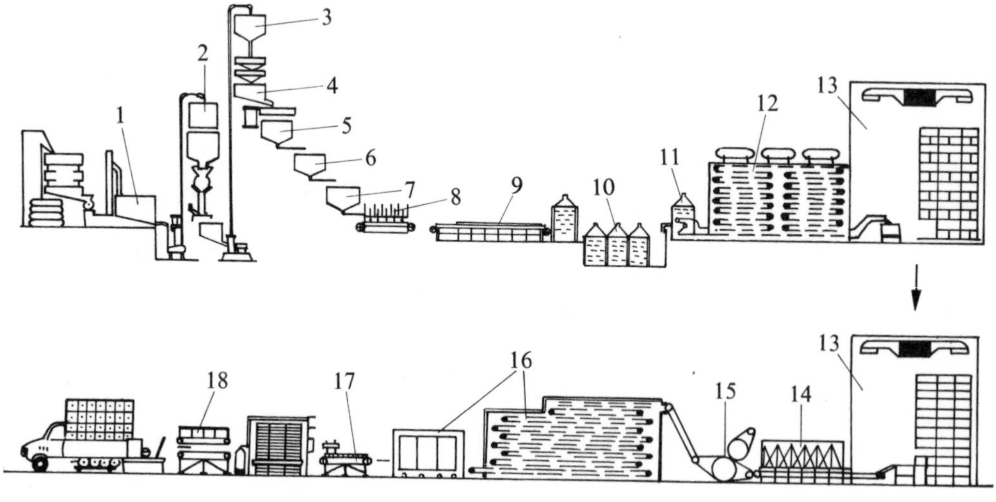

1—Soaking tank	7—Grinder	13—Frozen storage
2—Grinder	8—Molding box	14—Continuous thawing
3—Cooker	9—Dehydration	15—Press dehydration
4—Filter	10—Soaking	16—Drier
5—Soy milk	11—Cutter	17—Trimming
6—Coagulation tank	12—Freezing equipment	18—Packaging

treatment of whey and waste water streams. In the past, the insoluble residue (*okara*) from soy-milk production was widely used as animal feed, but the demand is now diminishing because of the growing popularity of various concentrated, composite feeds. Some people are attempting to dry it completely for use either in such composite feeds or as dietary fiber.

In Japan, from thirty to forty thousand tons of soybeans are used annually in the production of dried-frozen tofu. This amounts to no more than one-tenth that of fresh and deep-fried tofu products. Demand is not as large for dried-frozen tofu as for fresh tofu. The dried-frozen tofu is a traditional regional food—popular in soups, cooked with vegetables, and in sushi in western Japan—and shows little sign of gaining favor elsewhere. Furthermore, the current marked trend for diet variety helps account for its limited appeal. Automation and labor saving proceed apace in plants producing this food (Fig. 28). Four or five such plants are capable of using about ten tons of soybeans a day. Such large operations account for more than 60 percent of the total national product.

Soy Milk

Though the Chinese have long drunk it, the Japanese have traditionally regarded soy milk as no more than one stage in the manufacture of tofu. In recent years, however, considerations of the quality of the fat in cow's milk, the superior health value of vegetable oils, and cost have given rise to the marketing of more and more drinks based on soy milk. This drink has a distinctive odor, which the Chinese do

Fig. 29 Soy milk.

not find objectionable but which must be eliminated or disguised in any of several ways for the Japanese and for Westerners. People who are accustomed to drinking cow's milk apparently do not take well to the odor of soy milk.

As has already been explained in the section on making tofu, soy milk is prepared by soaking soybeans overnight in water, grinding them with additions of water, adding further water, heating the mixture to the boiling point, and then filtering. The amount of water required is determined by the desired concentration of the finished soy milk.

A number of methods have been devised for coping with the odor of this milk. In one method, the milk is heated with direct steam, which eliminates the odor-causing substances. But this method is only partly effective. In the hot-grinding method, heat is applied immediately after grinding to inactivate enzymes (Cornell University method). This is based on the argument that the odor of soy milk is a product of the action of the oxidizing enzyme called lipoxygenase on soybean oil at the instant the beans are ground. The effectiveness of the method is recognized, though it is said by some that steaming or boiling of the beans before grinding is still more effective (method of U.S. Department of Agriculture and the University of Illinois). But with such a system it is essential to control heating before soybean proteins become insoluble. With the development of soy-milk sterilization, aseptic packaging by means of tetra-brick containers has helped popularize soy milk (Fig. 30). Recently, in Japan, with the almost total elimination of the offensive taste, such big industries as dairy and oil manufacturers have begun producing soy milk, the output of which has rapidly increased, as much as doubling in a year. Contributing to this growth in production are the possibility of storing soy-milk products in refrigerators for at least two months and increased consumer interest in the physiological effects of soybean components on human health.

In the past few years in Japan, soy milk with flavor additives—fruit juice, coffee, vanilla, milk, and so on—have been marketed, as have soy-milk

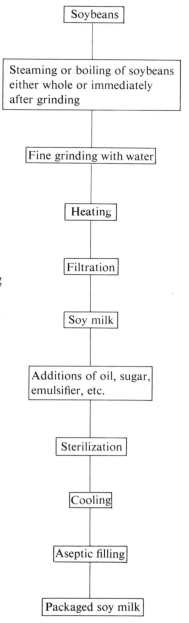

Fig. 30 Flow sheet for aseptically packaged soy-milk production.

drinks flavored and made slightly sour by stimulating the cultivation of lactic-acid bacilli. The JAS (Japan Agricultural Standard) for soy milk was issued two years ago. In addition, spray-dried soy milk is manufactured for use in the production of tofu and confections and as a meat filler as well as in beverages. As is true of dried cow's milk, dried soy milk must be blended with small amounts of water before being reduced to the desired concentration.

Yuba

A film forms on the surface of heated soy milk—just as on the surface of heated cow's milk. Gently lifted from the liquid and dried, the film becomes a product known as *yuba*, apparently originally introduced into Japan from China. Limited in use to such cuisines as vegetarian diets once prescribed for Buddhist priests, *yuba* is made in only moderate quantities. Composed of nourishing oil and protein, *yuba* deserves reconsideration as a solid soy-milk product.

Soy milk for *yuba* should have about 10 percent solids; that is, it should be of about the same concentration as the milk used in the production of silken tofu. In a thin, flat—often copper—pan, this milk is heated almost but not quite to the boiling point. When the film forms on the liquid surface, it is lifted off with two bamboo sticks and then dried partly or entirely. Generally, films should not be allowed to touch each other during the drying process. Heating of the milk is continued till it produces another film, which is removed and dried. As has been said, *yuba* consists largely of oil and protein—it contains some sugar too. As one film

Fig. 31   Yuba.

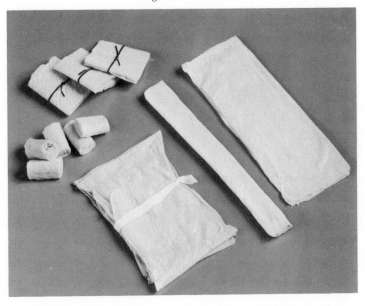

after another is lifted off, the protein and fat content of the milk drops. The outcome of this is weaker films of poor quality. The remaining liquid has a higher sugar content. To prolong the productivity of the process, from time to time, fresh soy milk is added. Sometimes, *yuba* is made of an entire batch of soy milk to which no additions of fresh milk are made. In such instances, the final product, called *matsuba-yuba* (pine-needle *yuba*), is of the lowest quality.

A kilogram of soybeans produces about 550 grams of dried *yuba*. Annually in Japan, a few hundred tons of soybeans are used in *yuba* manufacture in small plants dispersed in such places as Tokyo, Nikko, and Kyoto.

To increase consumption of this nutritious food, new dishes employing it and cheaper production methods must be devised. The Chinese use heat and pressure to bind together many layers of *yuba* into foodstuff that, when cut thin, closely resembles meat. This seems to offer a possibility for *yuba* consumption as something like simulated meat.

Roasted Soy Flour (*Kinako*)

A fragrant meal made by grinding whole, roasted soybeans is called *kinako* and is used in a wide variety of confections and as a coating for a favorite Japanese specialty made of pounded glutinous rice and known as *mochi*. The beans for *kinako* must be carefully selected and cleaned. Chinese soybeans are preferred for their flavor. Some *kinako* has a greenish cast resulting from the green cotyledon as well as green bean husk. The beans are first roasted. Traditionally this was done in a flat pan at a temperature of 160°C for from 10 to 20 minutes. More recently,

Fig. 32   Kinako

however, the kind of rotary roaster employed in roasting chestnuts has become popular. Gravel is added to ensure even heating, and the beans are roasted at 220°C for about 30 seconds. They are then ground in a high-speed grinder. In some instances the soybeans are cracked and hulled before grinding. This produces the best quality *kinako*. The powder is sieved through a metal screen (0.4 milli-meter mesh) fitted around the grinder. Annual *kinako* production is not large. This foodstuff, prepared in about 200 factories throughout the nation, demands approximately 6 thousand tons of soybeans each year. Most of the plants have a production capacity of about 80 kilograms daily, though large factories produc-ing *kinako* as calf feed can prepare more than 5 tons a day.

Dry roasting at high temperatures destroys harmful trypsin inhibitors and other elements causing physiological damage and improves the digestibility of the soy-bean protein. But overheating can destroy lysine, which is abundant in soybeans and is one of the essential amino acids. For example, exposure to 160°C for 10 minutes destroys part of the lysine; and exposure to the same temperature for only 5 minutes reduces available lysine content by 20 percent.

Soybean Sprouts

Most bean sprouts consumed in Japan are made from mung beans, but some are made from soybeans—especially those for use in Korean-style food. Cooked and eaten as vegetables, bean sprouts have a high water content and are rich in vitamin C.

To make bean sprouts, soybeans are first soaked in water (from 40°C to 50°C)

Fig. 33 Soybean sprouts.

for from 3 to 4 hours. Then they are spread in thin layers on concrete floors in dark rooms where the temperature is kept between 22°C and 23°C. Under these conditions, the beans germinate in about 24 hours. They are sprayed from time to time with water at a temperature of from 22°C to 24°C. In about a week the sprouts have reached a length of 10 centimeters. They are then washed, hulled, and bagged for shipment. In the past it was customary to add solutions of either 0.01 percent sodium hyposulfite or 0.3 percent calcium hypochlorite to prevent discoloration during storage by acting as a bleach. This practice has been discontinued in recent times.

Roughly from 7 to 9 kilograms of bean sprouts are produced from 1 kilogram of soybeans. Bean sprouts are relatively high in vitamin C: 23–44 mg (dry basis) percent compared to 0 percent (dry basis) in whole soybeans. Moreover, as a consequence of the germination process, free amino acids increase (20–200 times on a dry basis). Asparagine increases especially dramatically (more than 200 times).

4. *Miso and Other Fermented Soybean Products*

Miso

The most ordinary ingredients for the preparation of the fermented food called miso (bean paste) are soybeans, rice, and salt, though it is sometimes made of barley, soybeans and salt, or of soybeans and salt.

Preparation

The production of the *kōji* is of the greatest importance in making miso, which is prepared by steaming soybeans till they are soft; adding the *kōji*, salt, and water; and fermenting this mixture. Rice *kōji* is pre-

Fig. 34 Flow sheet for miso production.

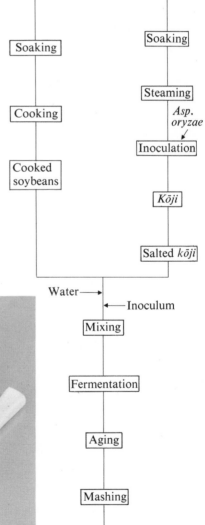

Fig. 35 Miso.

pared in the following way. Milled rice is thoroughly washed and cleaned. It is then soaked overnight in water. After soaking for from 17 to 20 hours in water at a temperature of from 17°C to 20°C, the rice will have absorbed enough water to increase its weight by 2.2 times. The rice is then drained and heated in a steamer called a *koshiki* fitted on a boiling kiln. The rice must be steamed evenly. But sometimes steam passages develop resulting in insufficiently steamed or even virtually unsteamed areas. To prevent this, the rice is put into the *koshiki* (Fig. 36) bit by bit; and steam is allowed to be drawn up through the steamer before each new addition. After the last addition, the lid is put in place; and the rice is steamed for the necessary length of time. The steamed rice must be resilient and softened to the center of each grain. Furthermore, it must be thoroughly gelatinized; and individual grains must not stick strongly to each other. Japanese rice will produce good *kōji* in one steaming of this kind. Low grade rice, especially imported cracked rice, which is now popular in miso making, must be steamed once for 15 minutes, removed from the container, and

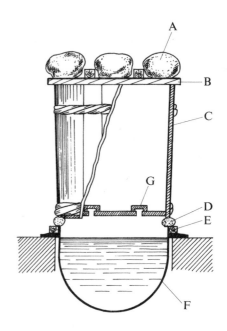

Fig. 36   *Koshiki* for rice cooking

A: weight
B: Cover
C: Cask
D: Straw ring
E: Frame
F: Pan
G: Steam inlet

Fig. 37   Continuous rice cooker.

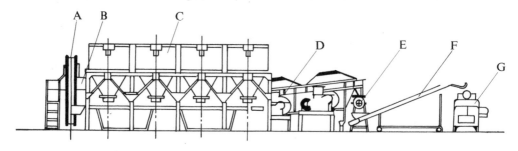

A: Soaked-rice conveyor
B: Rice-steaming machine
C: Soaking tank
D: Cooling machine

E: Mold inoculator
F: Belt conveyor
G: Scale

Fig. 38   Aspergillus oryzae.

Fig. 39   Kōji.

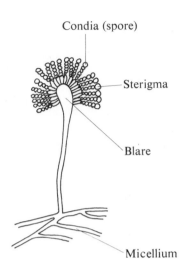

Condia (spore)

Sterigma

Blare

Micellium

allowed to cool till the surface is dry and cracked. It is then soaked in water again and finally steamed for from 30 to 60 minutes in the fashion used for one-steaming ordinary rice.

In more modern production systems, the soaked rice is steamed while being conveyed on a continuous moving metal shelf (Fig. 37). The steaming time may be adjusted by altering the speed of the conveyor. After steaming, the rice is cooled to from 30°C to 35°C. It is then moved to a *kōji* room, where the temperature is kept at 28°C, and inoculated with *Aspergillus oryzae* spores (Fig. 38), which are commercially available in a product called *tane-kōji*. The weight of the *tane-kōji* used is about 0.1 percent that of the steamed rice. After inoculation, the rice is covered with a cloth and allowed to stand for about 10 hours at a temperature of from 30°C to 35°C. During this time, the spores germinate gradually to produce a mycelium. The respiration heat of the mold raises the temperature. The mold is cultured for another 6 or 7 hours. When it has become still more active, it is transferred to wooden boxes (30 × 40 × 10 centimeters) called *kōji-buta* (*kōji*-tray). The amount of *kōji* per box, based on the weight of the original rice, is about 1.5 kilograms. When the amount of *kōji* being produced is large, boxes are so numerous that they must be stacked. But to ensure good ventilation for mold cultures, a special stacking system is used. During the day's storage period in the *kōji* room, the *kōji* must be regularly hand stirred to introduce fresh air and prevent the temperature from rising too high. From time to time, the boxes are restacked to ensure steady temperatures and ventilation. More than 40 hours are required for the completion of *kōji* (Fig. 39) from initial inoculation time.

In more up-to-date cultivation processes, the wooden boxes are not used at all because maintaining steady temperatures and distributing and stacking the boxes demand too much time and labor. Steamed rice mixed with *tane-kōji* is spread on a spacious floor (Fig. 40). Both temperature and humidity are carefully regulated as fresh, pure air is introduced to stimulate growth of *Aspergillus oryzae*, which reaches a peak after about 5 hours at a temperature of from 25°C to 27°C. The mixture must be stirred for ventilation and to break up lumps of *kōji*. The entire process is completed in about 40 hours. In another method, steamed rice inoculated with *Asp. oryzae* spores is put into a rotary fermenter and slowly revolved as warm air is blown on it.

Such enzymes as amylase and protease, abundant in *kōji*, act during the miso fermentation process to hydrolyze the starch and proteins in the rice and soybeans and in this way to account largely for the sweetness and good taste of the miso.

To break down soybean proteins in the production of miso, the *kōji* protease must be abundant. This means that the process takes longer than does the one used in sakè brewing. If the *kōji* is left as it comes from the *kōji* rooms, its temperature rises as a result of respiratory heat, which inactivates some of the enzyme and stimulates the growth of various other microorganisms. To prevent this, the *kōji* is mixed with sodium chloride. As a consequence, growth of the *Asp. oryzae* is halted; and the enzymes stored in them are released from the cells. The activity of these enzymes reaches a peak in about 2 or 3 days following salting.

The *kōji* will be mixed with soybeans. But before this is done, the beans must be soaked overnight and then steamed, preferably in a pressure cooker, which ensures tenderness and reduces cooking time. The beans are steamed at 115°C (0.75 kg/cm²) for from 20 to 40 minutes. If the beans are cooked in the kind of nonpressurized steamer used for rice, the process takes 6 or 7 hours. Modern plants use continuous steamers to move soaked soybeans along a screw conveyor while steam is supplied to them till cooking is completed.

Fig. 40 Fermentation room for *kōji* preparation.

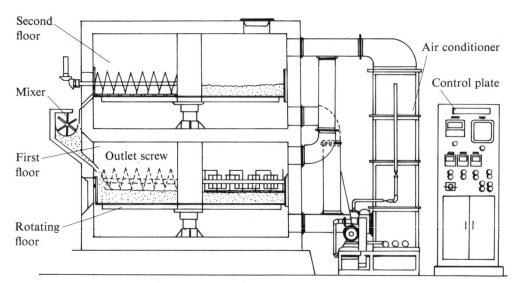

Fig. 41   Wooden cask for miso fermentation.

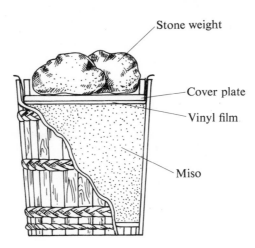

Stone weight

Cover plate

Vinyl film

Miso

In the past, to make certain they were thoroughly tender, steamed soybeans were left in a cooking vessel, without heat, overnight. This is less popular today since the standing period discolors the beans.

Sometimes to prevent darkening of the miso, soybeans are boiled instead of being steamed. Though this ensures greater tenderness than steaming does, it reduces the flavor of the finished product since flavor-producing substances are lost in the water. High-temperature, short-time steaming equipment is now available for the same purpose.

Because fewer soybeans are produced in Japan today, imported beans are now popular. Chinese beans are preferred for miso production because they are more flavorful and tender when steamed than most beans from the United States. But among American soybeans, there are some varieties that become tender when steamed and that are not inferior in flavor to the Chinese product.

After being reduced to room temperature—or a temperature near it—the steamed beans are mixed with salted *kōji* and water and put in vats or wooden casks (Fig. 41). In more recent times, it has become customary to run the mixture through a chopper before being packed in vats to speed up the maturation process. In some cases, salt added to the *kōji* at the salting stage is reduced and the remainder is added at this step. Sometimes the salted *kōji* is added while the steamed beans are still hot, and the steaming heat is used in maturation. In order not to alter the form of the *kōji*, the steamed beans may first be run through a chopper and then mixed with the salted *kōji*.

In modern plants, yeasts and lactic-acid bacteria as inoculants are added to the water mixed with the beans at this stage. In the past, wild yeasts and bacteria entered the mixture naturally from the surrounding air and were thought to account for the quality of the finished product. Today, however, to improve quality, pure cultures of known varieties are used. The yeasts used are salt-resisting yeasts called *Saccharomyces rouxii*, *Torulopsis* sp., *Pediococcus halophilus*, and a salt-resisting acid bacteria *Streptococcus faecalis* isolated from high-quality miso.

Thorough and uniform blending of *kōji*, steamed beans, salt, and water is of the utmost importance to ensure uniform fermentation and to introduce air to prevent the growth of anaerobic microorganisms. Traditionally a man with a shovel did this by manually transferring the mixture from one vat to another. In modern plants, however, the process is mechanized and may consist in either inverting the vat or vigorous stirring of a digging kind.

Fermentation can be carried out either naturally, using the temperatures of the surroundings, or with the artificial addition of heat. Since enzyme breakdown and microorganism growth fermentation take place actively only in summer in natural conditions, the former process always requires about 6 months and, depending on the time at which the mixture is set down to ferment, can take as much as a year. Before being marketed, miso that has been chopped so fine that the soybeans and rice cannot be distinguished from each other is mashed through a sieve (Fig. 42). But consumer demand has resulted in the production of some miso, in which it is possible to tell the beans from the rice.

Fig. 42 Mashing machine for miso.

As I have already mentioned, the *kōji* is sometimes mixed with the beans while they are still hot. This is done by wrapping the vats in straw mats or by surrounding them with insulating materials to maintain the original temperature. Another method of artificial heating is to keep the vat in a room at about 30°C. For the first few days, the vats are stored at room temperature, then steps are taken to raise the temperature. With this method, fermentation is complete in from 1 to 3 months, the length of time varying depending on the kind of miso being made.

Quantities of output too vary with kind of miso. But, in general, 1,000 kilograms of soybeans, 600 kilograms of rice, and 430 kilograms of salt will give about 3,700 kilograms of miso with a moisture content of roughly 50 percent. After fermentation, the miso was traditionally packed in barrels for shipment. Recently however, it has become more popular to pack it in plastic bags, which are then put in cardboard boxes or wooden barrels. For retail sale, miso is often packed in small plastic bags.

Since these small bags are hermetically sealed, enzymatic action in the product continues to produce carbon dioxide gas, which causes the bag to swell and thus lowers the commercial value of the product. To prevent this the miso must be pasteurized. Preheating proves effective in this connection, and equipment to carry it out has been developed. Additions of sorbic acid have a pasteurizing effect, but today the most popular method is a combination of heat and addition of from 1 to 2 percent ethyl alcohol.

As production scale has grown, the problem of disposing of wastes has arisen. Untreated water in which beans and rice have been washed pollutes the waters of rivers in the neighborhoods of miso factories. To prevent this, the most popular method is active sludge treatment; and most large factories are equipped to carry it out. But, since all the components of the waste are edible, it would be more reasonable to use them in food products. At present, attempts are being made to employ microbes originating from the cultivation of yeasts and molds in the wastes as material in the fermentation stage of miso production.

Kinds of Miso

Like cheeses in the West, misos of many different varieties have evolved under various local cultural and climatic conditions. Still the product can be widely classified according to major ingredient: rice miso, barley miso, or soybean miso. The preceding explanation was for the production of rice miso, in which rice and soybeans are the main ingredients. The rice may be replaced with milled barley at a rate of from 80 to 85 percent yield. Barley *kōji* is produced in a way similar to that used for rice *kōji*, though barley absorbs water faster and, since the grain is grooved, runs the danger of contamination by unwanted microorganisms. For this reason, selection of *tane-kōji* must be done with the greatest care. In both rice and barley miso, the higher the proportion of these two grains to that of soybeans, the smaller the amounts of salt used, and the shorter the fermentation time. Since both rice and barley have high starch contents, *kōji* enzymes act to produce sugar, which in turn gives the finished miso a sweet taste within a shorter fermentation time. So-called white miso—it is actually light yellow—contains a high ratio of rice (2 to 2.5 times as much rice as soybeans and 5 percent salt; its fermentation process is completed in about 10 days). For this product soybeans are boiled, not steamed, and the water in which they are boiled is discarded. White miso does not keep as long as other varieties and should be stored refrigerated. The miso called *Sendai-miso* is produced with a smaller amount of rice (about half the amount of soybeans) and a high percentage of salt (about 13 percent in the final product). Red, salty misos include *Sado*, *Echigo*, and *Tsugaru* miso. *Edo-miso* has the same amount of or slightly more rice than soybeans, contains 6 percent salt, and tastes fairly sweet. *Shinshū-miso* is pale-colored, salty miso with about half as much rice as soybeans. It ferments in a fairly short time, contains 12 percent salt, and has a slight sour taste.

The third major variety of miso is made from soybeans alone with no admixtures of rice or barley. The *kōji* is made directly from soybeans. Soaking water is limited to from 1.6 to 1.7 times the weight of the soybeans. The beans are steamed for 2 hours at a pressure of 0.4 kg/cm². After mashing, the beans are formed at 55°C into balls of from 10 to 40 millimeters in diameter. Machines make this task easier. The surfaces of the balls are inoculated with *Asp. oryzae*. The balls are then placed in wooden boxes (*kōji-buta*) or *kōji* room and kept warm while the *Asp. oryzae* are grown. Care must be taken to move them occasionally to ventilate them well. Finally the balls are crushed in a roller and mixed with water and salt to make soybean miso by fermentation. A miso called *Hatcho-miso* of this variety has a maturation period of as much as 2 years. It is blackish brown in color and slightly bitter in taste. It contains from 10 to 11 percent salt. A liquid exuded from the bottom of soybean miso during maturation is sometimes used as a kind of soy sauce called *tamari-zhōyu*. The remaining miso is called *tamari-miso*. But these products are rarely made today.

Miso Production in Japan

At present about 2,000 plants in Japan are engaged in the production of miso. Using annually from 170 to 180 thousand tons of soybeans and 100 thousand tons of rice, they produce about 560 thousand tons of miso. Though large-scale plants are increasing in numbers, there are still only about 30, or 1.5 percent of the total, capable of an annual output of more than 3,750 tons. Nonetheless, this 1.5 percent accounts for more than 50 percent of the total national miso output.

Composition of Miso

The composition of miso is shown in Table 4 on page 22. Hydrolysis of soybean proteins results in amino acids and peptides that account for the taste of miso. Maltose and glucose are produced from the starch in rice to account for sweetness. When these sugars are further broken down, they produce alcohols and organic acids that give miso its flavor. Hydrolysis of fats gives fatty acids that react with alcohol to produce esters and give the aroma of miso.

Miso and Mycotoxin

In about 1965, the possibility of the presence of aflatoxin in miso was seriously discussed since *Aspergillus oryzae*, used in the manufacture of *kōji*, is closely related to *Aspergillus flavus* known to produce aflatoxins, which have a strong carcinogenic action. Similar doubts were entertained about sakè and soy sauce, both of which employ *kōji*. Experiments conclusively proved, however, that none of these foods contain such toxins and that *Aspergillus oryzae* does not produce aflatoxins or other toxins generated by microorganisms.

Miso in Food

The average Japanese consumes about 20 grams of miso a day, most often in the form of miso soup (generally 1 percent salt content) served hot and enriched with vegetables (leafy vegetables, potato, *daikon* radish, onions, and so on); seaweeds, or tofu. Sometimes vegetables like cucumbers, eggplant, and *daikon* radish are pickled by being immersed for certain periods of time in miso. Meat or fish immersed in miso for relatively long periods lose their strong odors. Today an instant miso soup is marketed. Convenient since all that is necessary is to add hot water to the packaged ingredients, this product contains other lyophilized ingredients (seaweeds, vegetables, and so on). Though it is somewhat different in flavor from miso soup prepared from fresh miso, this instant food is nonetheless palatable. No startling changes occur in the qualities and colors of its ingredients owing to lyophilization.

Processed Miso

A number of products (called *namemiso*) consisting of miso with additions of such other ingredients as sugar and salt are commercially marketed. *Tekkamiso* is prepared in the following way. First burdock root is scraped, julienne cut, and soaked in water to remove astringency. It is then drained and thoroughly sautéed in sesame oil. Next washed soybeans, sesame seeds, and sliced lotus root are added. After this mixture has been well sautéed, miso is added together with sugar and a sweetened sakè called *mirin*. This is cooked till well done. It must be stirred regularly to prevent scorching.

Nattō

The Japanese fermented food called *nattō*, the production of which involves the action of the bacteria *Bacillus nattō*, goes well with steamed rice (foods similar to *nattō* are to be found in Thailand and Indonesia too). More popular in the eastern part of Japan, *nattō* is generally seasoned with soy sauce. Though small domestic soybeans are preferred, reductions in crops have made it necessary to rely on small Chinese beans or on beans that have been sift-graded. Selected beans are washed and soaked in water overnight. They are then cooked in a steamer or a pressure cooker (from 1 to 1.5 kg/cm^2) for from 20 to 30 minutes, or until they are about as soft as beans destined to be used in the manufacture of miso (Fig. 44). The steamed beans are then inoculated with a pure-culture suspension of *Bacillus nattō* and thoroughly mixed and allowed to be covered by the suspension (Fig. 45). Usually

Fig. 43 Nattō

from 5 to 10 milliliters of suspension is used with 60 kilograms of raw soybeans. The inoculated beans—in units of 100 grams—are put into polyethylene bags and then into shallow sliced-wood or polystyrene trays and set in a warm, thermostatic chamber for fermentation. The polyethylene bags are perforated from the outset for good ventilation. After from 14 to 20 hours at 40°C, the *Bacillus nattō* will have covered the beans with a white coating. Overfermentation releases ammonia, which spoils the flavor. In addition, ammonia may destroy the *Bacillus nattō* and promote spoilage and decay.

In the past, steamed beans were wrapped in containers made of rice straw. The wild *Bacillus nattō* living in the straw caused the fermentation that results in *nattō*. But since contamination by other unwanted microorganisms reduced the quality of the product, this method has been largely abandoned in favor of inoculation with pure-cultured *Bacillus nattō*. Dividing the steamed bean-mixture

Fig. 44 Pressure cooker for soybeans.

Fig. 45 Rotating mixer to combine cooked soybeans with pure-cultured *Bacillus nattō*.

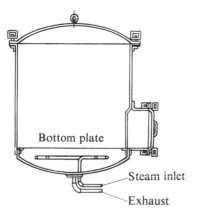

Bottom plate

Steam inlet

Exhaust

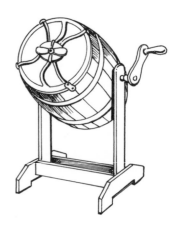

into 100-gram batches demands time and labor, but at present further automation is not being attempted. Temperature control in the fermentation vats is important. Since heat generated by the beans themselves during fermentation produces ammonia, automatic temperature control is desirable.

In the large plants that have recently developed in the Tokyo suburbs, *nattō* is stored under refrigeration to suppress fermentation and is taken out as needed.

Most of the roughly 1,000 *nattō*-producing plants in Japan daily consume less than 150 kilograms of soybeans. Large plants may require from 2 to 3 tons. The amount of soybeans used for *nattō* annually throughout the nation is from 70 to 80 thousand tons.

Table 4 on page 22 shows the composition of *nattō*. The white substance coating the beans in *nattō* is a polymer of glutamic acid that gives this food its characteristic sticky, stringy quality. During the fermentation process, breakdown of some of the constituents of the soybeans makes *nattō* easier to digest and more tasty. In addition, *Bacillus nattō* itself produces various enzymes helpful to good digestion. Some scholars insist that *nattō* contains an unknown element that stimulates growth and is essential to human physiology. As yet, however, this substance remains unidentified.

Small soybeans are preferred for several reason. First, they absorb water well, shorten steaming time, and result in high yield by reducing loss. Furthermore, they are easy to eat. Because of the larger surface areas involved in small beans as compared to larger ones, small-grain *nattō* contains more *nattō* bacillus.

Hama-nattō (Tera-nattō)

Though the names are similar, *nattō* and *Hama-nattō* are actually quite different. First of all, the microorganisms used to inoculate them are not the same. *Hama-nattō* is made from selected soybeans, wheat, salt, and ginger. The beans are soaked in water (20°C) for 3 or 4 hours and then drained and steamed for 5 or 6 hours. After being left to stand in the steaming vessel overnight, when they have reached a temperature of less than 40°C, the beans are mixed with toasted and ground wheat (sometimes barley) inoculated with so-called *tane-kōji*. This mixture is well blended and then distributed among shallow wooden boxes, which are stored at from 30°C to 35°C for 50 hours, until the culture has grown. The beans are then dried in the sun until a mixture that formerly contained from 30 to 35 percent water contains only from 20 to 25 percent. This mixture is then just covered with a brine (Baumé 15 degrees), lidded, weighted, and allowed to stand for from 6 to 12 months. (Sometimes soy sauce is used in place of brine.) The beans are then spread on linen and once again dried in the sun before finally being mixed with ginger that has been pickled in soy sauce.

Hama-nattō retains the shape of the original soybeans but is a lusterless blackish color. Very salty (about 10 percent) and with a low water content (from 36 to 38 percent) it keeps for a long time. *Hama-nattō* is a speciality of a place called Hamamatsu, in Shizuoka Prefecture immediately adjacent to Aichi Prefecture, which is famous for its soybean miso. Obviously there is a close relation between these products and *Hama-nattō*.

Soy Sauce

Long essential in the Japanese diet, soy sauce is now produced in plants in lands other than Japan and is becoming an internationally popular seasoning. The raw materials for soy sauce are soybeans, wheat, and salt. Since soybean oil floats to the surface of the liquid when fermentation is completed, defatted beans are now used from the outset (Fig. 47). Since the production of soy sauce involves only a liquid state, fermentation is more vigorous than in the case of miso production. The action of the enzymes in *Asp. oryzae* plus that of yeast and bacteria grown in soy sauce convert most of the proteins in the raw materials into amino acids. The starches in them are converted first into sugars and then into alcohols or organic acids, which partly form the flavor substances. With the production of alcohols and acids, carbon dioxide is produced and then lost in the air. The color of soy sauce is a principle product of amino carbonyl reaction resulting from the action of amino acids and reducing sugars. In this sense, it is produced in a way similar to that in which the color of miso is produced.

Fig. 46 Soy sauce.

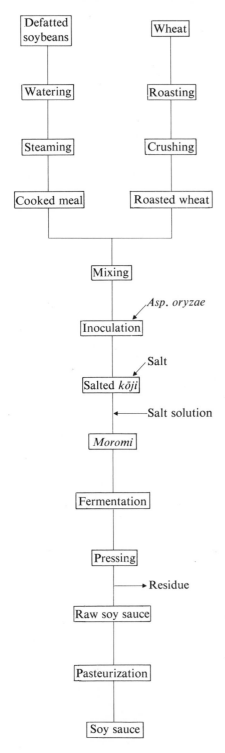

Fig. 47 Flow sheet for soy-sauce production

Manufacture

The *kōji* from which soy sauce is produced is made in the following way. Defatted soybeans are first steamed and then mixed with roasted, crushed wheat and inoculated with *Aspergillus oryzae* (*tane-kōji*). The mixture is then transferred to storage rooms (called *kōji* rooms) where the mold is allowed to grow.

To prepare soy-sauce *kōji*, defatted soybean flakes (Nitrogen Solubility Index from about 30 to 60) are carefully cleaned. All foreign matter is removed. The flakes are sprinkled with water (30 percent of their own weight), and the mixture is steamed. In large factories, pressure steamers may be used (0.95 kg/cm² for about 45 minutes). Since rapid cooling after steaming is essential, suction pressure-reduction devices (NK kettles) are widely employed. Speed in cooling is needed to avoid lowering nitrogen availability. Furthermore, rapid cooling prevents the introduction of unwanted microorganisms. In some instances, pressure kettles are replaced by continuous-operation equipment for all processes from sprinkling to steaming.

The wheat is first toasted to dry, sterilize, and gelatinize its starch. When it is brown, it is crushed in rollers until more than 20 percent of it will pass through a 30-mesh screen (Fig. 48). This is necessary if the wheat is to absorb adequate moisture from the surface of the steamed, defatted soybeans. The beans and wheat are mixed; and, when their temperature has dropped suitably, they are inoculated with *tane-kōji*. As is true in the production of miso, large volumes of this mixture spread directly on the floor of the *kōji* room must be stirred at regular intervals for ventilation and to ensure uniform density. Precise temperature control now makes possible the

Fig. 48 Crusher (roller) for roasted wheat used in soy-sauce production.

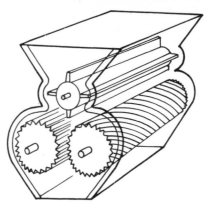

production of what is called 3-day *kōji*, which is incubated for 48 hours instead of 72 hours (4-day *kōji*) as in the case of the traditional wooden-tray method.

Because the major aim of the succeeding maturation period is decomposition of soybean protein by *kōji* proteases, it is desirable that the soy-sauce *kōji* be rich in these enzymes, which break protein down. In many cases, such *kōji* is coated with yellow mycelia. Today rotating containers, described in the section on miso production, are sometimes used for *kōji* preparation.

Kōji thus prepared is next mixed with brine and poured into tanks (Fig. 49). For a mixture consisting of 1,200 kilograms each of wheat and defatted soybeans, 4,230 liters of brine (19°Bè and 23.1 percent salt) are required. The salinity of the brine (warm water and raw salt) must be accurate. The mash or mixture of *kōji* and brine is called *moromi*. It must be stirred thoroughly to ensure solution uniformity. It is kept at 15°C for a month. The temperature is then raised to 28°C for 5 months and then lowered again to 15°C. Fermentation takes from 8 to 12 months; in other 72 hours (4-day *kōji*) as in the case of the traditional wooden-tray method. words, *moromi* set to fesment in April can be finished within the same year under natural condition. During fermentation, compressed air injections are performed to ensure uniformity and to keep the mash in an aerobic state to prevent the culture of unwanted microorganisms. When fermentation is complete, the mash is squeezed in a hydraulic or other device to separate the liquid from the dregs. The *moromi* can be put in nylon bags, which are stacked on each other and then psessed from above until the remaining dregs have a moisture content of 30 percent. If whole soybeans are used in the process, at this stage soybean oil floats to the surface in the form of ethyl esters, derivative fatty acids, and must be removed. Elimination of this step is the reason for using defatted beans.

The raw soy sauce resulting from the process to this point must be pasteurized to inactivate enzymes and destroy unwanted microorganisms. This is done by raising the temperature to from 65°C to 80°C. If precipitates form, they are filtered off. Heating can cause a change or loss of flavor-producing substances. But large soy-sauce manufacturers reduce this danger by using plate heaters, which

Fig. 49 Soy-sauce fermentation tank (outdoor).

safely raise the temperature of the raw soy sauce in a short time, thus adequately achieving such goals as pasteurization.

After pasteurization, the soy sauce is poured into containers: 2-liter bottles, plastic containers holding from 100 to 200 milliliters, or 18-liter wooden kegs. With reduction of family sizes, the 2-liter bottle is losing popularity since a small family takes about a month to consume this quantity and leaving the container opened for such long time has adverse effects on flavor. Consequently, manufacturers are turning out more smaller containers (100 to 200 milliliters).

Preservatives used in soy sauce include sodium-benzoate and paraoxy-benzoate (mainly butyl ester) in standard amounts of 0.6 g/l and 0.25 g/l respectively. In Japan, paraoxy-bensoate is mainly used for saving the cost. Since paraoxy-benzoate ester does not dissolve readily in water, it must be mixed with 4 times its own weight of a 5-percent solution of caustic soda, gradually raised to a temperature of 80°C, added drop by drop to the soy sauce, and then thoroughly mixed. Because paraoxy-benzoate separates and loses effectiveness if exposed to air for a long time, it is advisable to add it to soy sauce as quickly as possible. Sodium-benzoate, which does not require heating to high temperautres, is a good preservative for *tamari* soy sauce, which reacts unfavorably to heat, and for soy sauce to be exported to nations where paraoxy-benzoate is not permitted.

Soy sauce relying on natural temperature changes for fermentation requires about a year to mature. But it is said that soy sauce manufactured under the artificially accelerated system already mentioned (1 month at 15°C, 4 months at 28°C, and 1 more month at 15°C) is equal in flavor to those fermented in the traditional way. A ton of defatted soybeans, a ton of wheat, and a ton of salt produce 5 thousand liters of soy sauce (specific gravity of 1.18).

Japanese Production

In the roughly 1.25 million tons of soy sauce made annually in Japan, from 170 to 180 thousand tons of both defatted soybeans and wheat are used. Of this total production, 5 large firms account for 50 percent; small and moderete plants produce the remainder. Each Japanese citizen consumes an average of about 30 grams of soy sauce daily; this quantity tends to remain constant.

Nitrogen Availability

The amount of the protein (nitrogen) carried over from raw materials like defatted soybeans into completed soy sauce is referred to as the nitrogen availability and is a highly significant value since it indicates the efficiency with which raw materials are used. In the past, the availability was usually given as 70 percent. But, with the realization that a number of factors affect this value—for instance, heating condition of defatted beans, variety of *Asp. oryzae* used, and fermentation conditions—it became possible to improve production processes to increase the availability to 80 percent. It was learned that overheating defatted soybeans drastically lowers nitrogen availability. NK kettles are effective in preventing overheating. Further, pretreatment with hydrochloric acid raises nitrogen availability. Still later, the development of high-temperature, short-time heating apparatus and such other steps as microorganism selection and adjustments of fermentation conditions have raised the nitrogen availability to 90 percent.

Kinds of Soy Sauce

In addition to the orthodox version (*koi-kuchi*), Japan produces several local varieties of soy sauce. Western Japan manufactures so-called light soy sauce (*usu-kuchi*), which is paler in color than the standard product and which is made from boiled, not steamed, whole soybeans. The pale color results from throwing away the water in which the beans were boiled and thus minimizing colored products resulting from amino-carbonyl reactions. The sauce called *tamari*, which is darker than the ordinary, is made from either entirely whole soybeans or entirely defatted soybeans with no wheat at all.

A solution of amino acids mixed with natural soy sauces to increase their volumes without decreasing nitrogen content is prepared by effecting complete hydrolysis of defatted soybeans by heating them 8 to 10 hours in 18-percent hydrochloric acid and then neutralizing with caustic soda. The resulting liquid is tastier than naturally fermented soy sauce, has less aroma, and is marred by a strange odor. It cannot be used as a complete replacement for the natural product.

Composition and Quality

As is seen in Table 4 (chemical composition; p. 22), soy sauce contains low-molecular-weight nitrogen compounds or protein calculated as $N \times 5.71$. In fact, soy sauce contains mainly amino acids and no true proteins at all. In addition to flavor and color, N content is a criterion for judging soy-sauce quality: a sauce containing 1.5 percent nitrogen is considered excellent according to the Japan Agriculture Standards.

Sufu

Though not produced in Japan, *sufu* is made in many parts of China from the central region to the vicinity of the southern seashore and especially in Fujian and Zhejiang provinces. It is made on Taiwan as well. *Sufu* is made by preparing fairly stiff tofu (using calcium chloride or more than the usual amount of calcium sulfate as a coagulant). The coagulant and soy milk mixture is stirred, transferred to molds, and pressed until its water content is about 70 percent. It is then inoculated with microorganisms and set to age in a mixture of miso, soy sauce, and Chinese wine. Before inoculation, the tofu is cut into cubes 3 centimeters to a side. The traditional way to inoculate was to put the tofu on rice straw or *igusa* rushes and to allow the wild *Mucor* (sometimes *Rhizopus*) microorganisms to form and grow naturally. Today, however, suspensions or dried powders of spores of pure-cultured microorganisms are used. Once inoculated, the cubes of tofu are transferred to the fermentation room, where they are kept at high humidity at 20°C for 2 or 3 days until the microorganisms have covered the tofu entirely. The cubes are then

Fig. 50 Sufu.

placed in miso or Chinese wine or miso or soy-sauce *moromi*, tightly sealed, and allowed to mature in a cool, dark place for from several months to a year. At the end of the maturation period, the tofu is removed and put on sale in containers filled with a *moromi*. Fully matured *sufu* will keep unspoiled for months. Commercially marketed *sufu* packed in cans, bottles, or ceramic containers is highly salty and usually additionally flavored.

From 1 kilogram of soybeans, 3 kilograms of fresh tofu may be made. This will produce 1.7 kilograms of inoculated tofu, which will in turn give about 2 kilograms of *sufu*. The red variety of *sufu* is made by adding red *kōji* produced by introducing the mold *Monascus* to steamed rice. A product called *tōfuyō*, which though different, closely resembles *sufu*, is made on Okinawa.

Tempeh

The Indonesian food *tempeh* is made by soaking soybeans in water, boiling them for an hour, cooling them to 40°C, inoculating them with *Rhizopus* spores, and piling them up to submit them to prefermentation for several hours. They are then put into containers (traditionally banana leaves but today more often plastic or metal containers) and allowed to ferment at 30°C for 2 or 3 days. Care must be taken to ensure that the temperature does not rise too high during fermentation. At the conclusion of this process, the surface of the beans and the interstices among them will be covered and filled with a white mycelium. About 1.7 kilograms of *tempeh* can be produced from 1 kilogram of soybeans. Since the water content is as much as from 55 to 60 percent, if left untreated, *tempeh* continues to ferment until it is spoiled by the generation of an ammonia odor. It must therefore be kept at a low temperature. To prevent spoilage it is sometimes dried or stored in salt. In recent times, with sun drying, hot-air blowers have come into use for drying, and can reduce the water content to about 4 percent. Consequently, *tempeh* can be kept for several months.

Because the fermentation time is short, the breakdown of the components in *tempeh* does not proceed very far. But amino acids are formed, and about one-third of the fat undergoes hydrolysis. Though the amount of vitamin B_1 is reduced, microorganism action causes an increase in B_2, B_6 and nicotinic acid. In dried *tempeh*, oxidation of fats and oils is retarded, and the presence of a substance causing antioxidation has been recognized. This is thought to result from the breakdown of isoflavone by microorganisms. In other words, *tempeh* has an antioxidative power that makes it useful as an antioxidant of oils and fats.

An excellent source of proteins in the Indonesian diet, *tempeh* is not eaten as it is but, after having been cut in slices from 1 to 2 centimeters thick, is seasoned and fried in coconut oil.

Though still in small amounts, *tempeh* is now produced in Japan from pure-cultured molds.

5. Other Ways of Eating Soybeans —Simple Traditional Japanese Foods

The complicated processes described in the preceding pages indicate how difficult it can be to prepare soybeans for use as human food. Today many of the soybean foods that once were prepared in Japanese homes are largely commercially manufactured and sold. But a few simple home foods persist in some parts of Japan, and this chapter offers brief explanations of a number of them.

Parched beans
Parched gently in unglazed ceramic dishes made for the purpose, soybeans can be fragrant, and palatable. Since the parching removes some of the hull, the beans become friable and crunchy. During a holiday called Setsubun, occurring in February, people toss parched soybeans around their houses while chanting "Demon out! Good luck in!" Then they pick up the beans and eat them. Parched beans are included in some varieties of *mochi* (glutinous rice cake) and in *okoshi* a confection made of puffed rice bound together with sugar syrup. In the past, they were eaten with salt, miso, or soy sauce.

Boiled beans
Soybeans that have been allowed to stand overnight in water are boiled for a long time until tender and then seasoned. As has been mentioned, boiling produces color and aroma. Boiled soybeans flavored with soy sauce and sugar are still sold under the name of *budo-mame* (grape beans). Sometimes the beans are not soaked overnight and are boiled only enough to remove the raw odor. These are then eaten flavored with soy sauce. For this dish, bean varieties (*hitashi-mame*) that absorb water readily are preferred.

Beaten and mashed soybeans
Since soaking and boiling take time, soybeans are sometimes crushed flat on a stone surface—in some instances after having been soaked or boiled. The beaten beans are cooked together with rice, boiled, or used in soups. As well as being crushed one by one, soybeans are mashed into a gritslike material in mortars. When soaked soybeans are ground, mixed with water, and boiled, the resulting substance is called *go* (soy purée), which, after having been filtered to eliminate solid residue, can be used as soy milk or to make tofu. *Go* itself is employed as

food. It may be added to miso soup, poured as a dressing on vegetables, or used as a substitute for red bean *an* (sweet paste). When fresh green soybeans (*edamame*) are used in cooking, they are boiled for from ten to twenty minutes; ground; and flavored with salt, sugar, and soy sauce. The resulting dish is called *zunda* or *jinda*.

Molded soybean mash

Soybean meal may be mixed with water and molded into semicircular small loaves that are then sliced, cooked, and flavored with salt or sugar. These slices were popular in western Japan. A similar effect can be made by water-grinding soybeans that have been allowed to soak in water overnight. The resulting mash may be formed into dumplings or other shapes, skewered, and grilled. In some parts of Japan, dumplings of this kind are used in miso soup. Though not the same as tofu, molded mashed soybeans are in some respects similar and for this reason are called *jinta-dōfu*.

Molded mashed soybeans and rice flour

Soybeans that have been lightly boiled are then allowed to stand in water 2 or 3 days. Next they are mixed with rice flour and ground in a mortar. They are then formed into rodlike shapes called *shitogi* that may be sliced and either eaten as they are or toasted. In this case, the rice flour is made digestible by repeated grinding.

Soybean-mash paste

Crushed or ground soybeans, mixed with a little water and some salt, are put down to ferment in lidded ceramic jars or other suitable containers. Barley *kōji* added to the mixture causes rapid fermentation since the beans have been crushed. The soybean-mash paste is said to be ready to eat in about a week.

6. *New Soybean Protein Products*

Defatted Soybeans

Before the defatting process, the soybeans are lightly dried by means of heat applications. They are then cracked (1/8–1/6 of the original beans), hulled by means of an aspirator, and flaked between large rollers while still hot to thicknesses of from 0.20 to 0.25 millimeters. Oil is then extracted by means of hexane (purified hydrocarbon from petroleum with a boiling point of 69°C). The soybean flakes are drained; and hexane, free fatty acids, color, and odor compounds are then removed from the crude oil to produce pure soybean oil. The flaked soybeans are repeatedly treated with hexane to ensure extraction of the maximum amount of oil. Then the beans are mildly heated to evaporate the hexane, leaving defatted soybean meal, the coarseness of which can be adjusted to suit the use for which the product is intended. The degree of protein denaturation directly affects the quality of defatted soybean meal. As has already been explained, the criteria for judging this are Nitrogen Solubility Index (NSI) or Protein Dispersibility Index (PDI). Since hexane has a low boiling point, slight increases in temperature and reduction of pressure are usually sufficient to eliminate it entirely. In such cases, the NSI remains very near that of raw whole soybeans, which means that protein denaturation does not take place. A low NSI reflects changes in the basic nature of the proteins and alteration of their functionality. But since, for animal feed, the trypsin inhibitor must be destroyed, heat treatment is used on defatted soybean meal; and the NSI is lowered. In the United States, minimum toasting results in meal with an NSI between 85 and 90; light toasting, a meal with an NSI between 40 and 60; moderate toasting, a meal with an NSI between 20 and 40; and full toasting, a meal with an NSI between 10 and 20. Meals are further graded according to coarseness: flour is the finest and is below 100 mesh. Coarser meals are called grits and occur in the following grades: fine (50 to 80 mesh U.S. standard screens), medium (20 to 50 mesh), and coarse (10 to 20 mesh). The United States further produces meals with various degrees of oil content. Low fat flour is defatted soybean flour to which oil has been added. Lecithinated soybean flour has added lecithin. Soybean meal from which no oil at all has been extracted is called full-fat soybean flour. Today in Japan continuous automated equipment makes it possible to use the hexane extraction method to process more than from 200 to 1,000 tons in a day. Sometimes benzine is used in extracting oil from soybeans. But, since benzine (a mixture of aliphatic hydrocarbons) has a high boiling point, high-temperature steam is necessary and their NSI is lowered. Consequently,

Fig. 51   Relations among the various new soybean-protein foods.

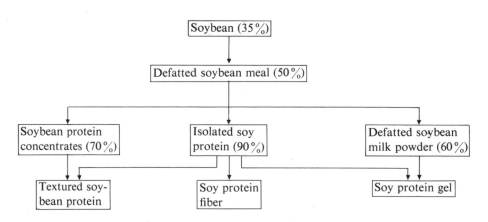

Protein content on a dry basis (%).

this method is not used when the finished products are intended to be used as foods for which functionality is important. The use of ethyl alcohol as a solvent removes not only oil, but also some of the sugars from soybeans and partly eliminates their flavor and odor. But because of the denaturation of proteins caused by ethyl alcohol, this system too is little used, except in the production of some minor products. Research has been conducted on finding ways to put to use the protein danaturation that ethyl alcohol causes.

Various new soybean-protein products are made from defatted soybean meal (Fig. 51).

Soybean-protein Concentrate

Since their protein content (50 percent) is higher than that of whole soybeans, dafatted soybeans themselves can be considered a protein concentrate. But in this case the words *soybean-protein concentrate* refers to the product resulting from the further increase of protein content by the elimination of such components as sucrose and other soluble carbohydrates.

The following methods may be used to accomplish removal of soluble elements from defatted soybeans and retain proteins and insoluble polysaccharides.

A)   Treat the defatted soybeans with ethyl alcohol (50 to 80 percent) to remove sugars and other alcohol-soluble components and then remove the alcohol by evaporation. In addition to part of the proteins, this removes peptides, amino acids, and the majority of inorganic matter. An example of the application of this method in the United States is a system whereby ethanol is added to hexane-wet soybeans that have been defatted with hexane. After the remaining lipids have been extracted by the hexane-alcohol, the hexane is distilled away. Then the sugars in the defatted meal are extracted with aqueous ethyl alcohol. Soybean-protein concentrates is then obtained after separation of the ethanol.

B) Treat defatted soybean flakes or flour with a weak acid solution till they reach a pH of 4.5 where the sugars and other soluble components will be extracted and removed. Most of the proteins will not be soluble at a pH of 4.5, though some proteins, together with peptides, amino acids, and inorganic substances will be soluble and eliminated. The residue may either be dried as it is or dried after being neutralized.

C) Steam defatted soybeans to denature the protein till it is insoluble in water and then extract and eliminate all substances other than the proteins by means of water treatment. In this instance, sugars associated with proteins will not be extracted. Other problems related to this method are the inevitable alteration in protein quality caused by steaming and an odor produced by the application of heat.

On a dry basis, the resulting products contain 70 percent (N × 6.25) protein and are therefore called protein concentrates. The second method is recommended because it causes less denaturation of the protein. The first and second methods are good because they eliminate the characteristic beany odor.

In the wider sense, the term *soybean-protein concentrates* cover products in which insoluble cellulose and hemicellulose have been removed from defatted soybeans. Treating defatted soybean with water or hot water to extract soluble matter and then filtering out insoluble substances and concentrating and drying the filtrate produce in a substance comparable to dry soy milk made from whole soybeans, except that it is oil-free. It has dry-basis protein content (N × 6.25) of about 60 percent.

In Japan, a soy-protein curd is made from concentrated proteins resulting from the second method. A mixture of defatted soybeans and water is heated to extract the protein and other soluble substances. To the heated mixture is added calcium salt (sometimes acid) to cause the proteins to precipitate. The protein and insoluble fibrous substances are filtered out from the soluble materials and, resembling a mixture of tofu and *okara*, is called soy-protein curd because it is not dried. It is, nonetheless, a concentrate of soybean protein since it is made from defatted beans. It must be stored at above 0°C, because it loses water-holding ability if it freezes. It was developed to mix with minced fish flesh for producing fish jelly products.

Isolated Soybean Protein

Theoretically isolated soybean protein should have a protein content of 100 percent. In fact, however, it is from 90 to 95 percent pure. To produce it, defatted soybeans with a high NSI (over 90) are selected and treated with water or alkaline (final pH value 7 to 9) to extract soluble materials. The resulting product is then centrifuged to eliminate insoluble materials. Hydrochloric acid (sometimes acetic acid) is added to the extract to bring it to a pH value of 4.5 and thus to cause precipitation at the isoelectric point. The solution is poured into decanters and centrifuged to separate the top liquid, which corresponds to whey in cheese and tofu production. After repeated water washings, the protein is air dried, or it may be suspended in water and then spray dried. Sometimes the protein is neutralized with alkali solution before spray drying. Unneutralized isolated proteins do not dissove in water. Those that have been neutralized, however, dissolve easily in water and form a gel when heated after being mixed with water. Thus they have wide functional possibilities. The several processes involved in the production of isolated soy proteins resemble those used in the production of tofu. It is important to minimize loss in the process in which the residue must be removed and to ensure yield, sanitary conditions, and noncontamination of the finished product.

Textured Soybean Protein

Textured soybean proteins are versions of the products outlined above processed to give them certain special characteristics, notably the texture and resilience desired in foodstuffs. Treatment of defatted soybeans or soybean protein concentrates with extrusion cookers produces the textures of processed meat products. Extrusion textured proteins are distinct from fibrous proteins, which will be explained later. The raw material is first steamed to give it a water content of from 15 to 40 percent. On occasion, alkali or salts are added at this time. This substance is then submitted to thermoplastic extrusion to orient the protein molecules when they emerge from the dies of the extruder. For this reason, the product will split easily only in the direction in which it emerges from the machine. Upon its emergence, the great pressure applied to it is suddenly lowered, causing it to expand. Reduction of moisture during expansion partially dries the textured materials. When defatted soybeans are the raw material, washing with water after extrusion will partially eliminate the flavor, odor, and sugars. This does not dissolve the proteins, which have been rendered insoluble. Adjustments of extruder nozzles and of cutter speeds make possible free selection of textured-protein form and length to suit the nature of the meat product with which it is to be used. Recent advances have resulted in equipment permitting double extrusion producing layered structures still closer to the texture of meat products. After having been artificially colored and flavored, textured soy proteins are added to ground meat or to sausages and processed meats. Sometimes, however, they are used to make simulated meat products that contain no meat at all. Two other methods of producing textured proteins in the United States are steam texturization and modified extrusion with a cooling die.

In the former method, defatted soybeans are treated with high-pressure steam to expand them and, in a short time, to eliminate more of the parched odor and color than is possible in the cooking-extrusion method and to lower water content. The latter system is similar to the cooking-extrusion method except that coolers fitted at the nozzles of the extruder prevent escape of steam and increase the density of the product.

Fibrous Soybean Protein

Textured soybean protein made of fine protein fiber is called fibrous or sometimes spun soybean protein. To produce meatlike textures, these fibers are bundled together and submitted to surface treatment or otherwise attached to other kinds of proteins. Isolated soy proteins are the raw material because fibers are difficult to form with materials with low protein content. Soybean proteins dissolved in an alkaline solution called dope are extruded through fine holes into an acid bath to form fine threads. The dope contains 14 to 18 percent protein, and its pH is 10 to 11. It is forced through a perforated metal disc called a spinnerette into an acidic bath containing sodium chloride. The acid coagulates the protein, which is immediately pulled to form fine threads, slightly stretched, and rolled up. The stretching orients the protein molecules to produce fibrous characteristics. Adjustments must be made to produce the desired fiber thicknesses and strengths, which influence chewability. The fibers are not dried before the next stage of processing, though sometimes they are frozen.

Another method of producing soy-protein fibers is less chemical and more physical than this one. Isolated or concentrated soy protein is mixed with water and submitted to high-heat treatment under high pressure. It is then extruded through small holes. Though the fibers resulting from this method are thicker than those produced in the previously described chemical method, they have marked interior orientation and are therefore closer to animal tissues in structure.

Applications of Isolated, Textured, and Fibrous Soybean Proteins

Isolated, textured, and fibrous soybean proteins are used as basic materials in foodstuffs. There are two ways of using soybean protein products for foods. The first is to use them in fairly small amounts as food additives to improve production processes and quality and to lengthen product shelf-life. Such applications were initiated before World War II. The second is to use them as substitutes or extenders of such meat products as sausages, processed meats, and meat loaf. These methods have been developed in the past two decades. In addition, soy proteins are employed in the manufacture of foodstuffs that contain no meat at all. Since in all cases, animal fats are either low or absent, people in the West regard these foods as wholesome and low-calorie additions to the diet.

When mixed with water and heated, isolated soy protein gels. Since in this respect it resembles minced fish flesh, an important material in a number of Japanese foods, it is used as a supplement, like wheat gluten, in the manufacture of fish jelly products. Neutralized isolated soy protein is preferred because of its higher gelling capacity. At one time, concentrated soy-protein curd was advanced for this kind of application, but its use was greatly decreased owing to low gelling capability.

The same gelling properties make isolated protein increasingly popular in the production of processed meats. The isolated protein is dissolved in a salt solution and injected into the meat product, which is then heated. The gelling of the protein increases the weight and yield, improves water-holding capacity, and prevents coalescence of oils in emulsion.

For use in meat products, textured or fibrous proteins must be selected depending on the variety of the meat product. Textured protein already has a texture resembling processed meat, but fibrous protein must be processed to simulate processed meat. Textured or fibrous protein must be flavored and colored with substances that must be absorbed by the protein. Textured and fibrous proteins are immersed in the seasonings, flavoring, and coloring solution for a definite time and then dehydrated by pressing or centrifugation. Coloring substances must be tightly bound with the protein, but seasonings and flavoring substances must be properly absorbed by the protein and should be gradually released from it during chewing.

It is more difficult to flavor and color these proteins when they are used in products containing no natural meat and fish than when they are mixed with these natural ingredients. Foods without natural ingredients include a dried product made to resemble bits of fried bacon, which is marketed in the United States, and products resembling corned beef and fish flakes (soboro), which are sold in Japan. Some of these Japanese products are specified by the Japan Agricultural Standards. In Japan, by mixing with oil, emulsion curd is made from the isolated soy protein. It is used to make tofu- and abura-agè-like products which are contained in dried and frozen foods. The products keep their original texture even after drying or freezing.

Since 1972, when the U.S. Department of Agriculture authorized their inclusion (30 percent of the rehydrated product) in school lunches, the use of textured soybean proteins in meat products has immensely increased in the United States. At one time, they were included in ground meats sold in American markets. But this is no longer true, and textured soy proteins are limited to use in school lunches, in catered foods and in processed meats.

In the ordinary preparation of humburger patties or meat loaf, loss of liquid causes the food to shrink during cooking. This can be prevented by the addition of textured soybean proteins at the mixing stage. These proteins absorb moisture, thus preventing both loss of liquid content and shrinkage. This step is taken in the

Table 5   Production of soybean protein products in Japan (t)

1975	1976	1977	1978	1979	1980	1981
13,259	15,775	16,958	21,176	20,792	26,270	28,208

Note: Products include defatted soybean meal; soybean protein concentrate; soybean protein isolate; textured soybean protein, and fibrous soybean protein.

Table 6   Production and price of soybean protein products in the United States (1982)

Product	Annual production 1,000 metric tons	Selling price* $/kg
Defatted flours and grits	159	0.31–0.33
Concentrates	36	0.88–1.32
Isolates	41	2.42–2.97
Textured flours	43	0.59–0.77
Textured concentrates	4	1.32

* May, 1983

preparation of not only domestic and catered foods, but also retorted pouched food products at the heating stage. Table 5 shows recent annual production of various soy protein products in Japan and Table 6 shows price and annual output of these products in United States.

Other Food Uses of Soy-protein Products

To improve quality and production process, small amounts of soy proteins are included in some kinds of bread and other foods, with the effect of increasing protein content in the finished food. These uses correspond to those developed in the United States before World War II.

Bread
Adding soybean protein, especially defatted soybeans, to bread was studied more than thirty years ago. Major causes for interest in this kind of addition were the needs to supplement low quantities of lysine in wheat protein and to prevent retrogradation of starches in bread during storage. Since soy protein is high in lysine it is an important bread supplement and significant material in the diets of all those developing nations where wheat is a stable food. The value of additions of this substance is now widely recognized since a supplement of 3 percent soy protein to wheat flour raises its lysine quantity by from 30 to 40 percent. Soy protein greatly lengthens the amount of time it may be stored without reduction in quality. Because of their good water-holding properties, defatted soybeans absorb moisture from starches and thus prevent their retrogradation. Further, because it is a good nutrient source for yeast, soy flour improves fermentation in bread and

thereby has a good effect on flavor and quality. For this purpose, heat-treated defatted soybeans, in which enzymes have been inactivated, are preferred. There is an exception to this statement, however. The enzyme lipoxygenase in unheated defatted soybeans breaks down the yellow carotinoids present in wheat flour. Therefore, when white bread is important, it is better to use soybeans in which the proteins have not been denatured by heat.

Care must be taken not to add too much defatted soybeans to bread batches, or the tensile strength of dough will be reduced; and the volume of the finished product will decrease. Research has shown that addition of 12 percent defatted soybeans to wheat flour can, if such steps are taken as the further addition of such surfactants as sodium stearoyl-2-lactylate, produce bread that is not inferior to bread to which no soybeans have been added.

Sausages
Because of their emulsifying action, defatted soybeans or isolated soy proteins prevent separation of fats in sausages. During production of fatty sausages, fat can accumulate and localize, thus lowering the commercial value of the product. Water loss during smoking is less when the binder in sausages is defatted soybeans (3–4 percent) than when other binding materials are used. This same high water-holding capability is found in isolated soy proteins as well.

Confections
Added to the wheat flour used in making such fried confections as doughnuts, defatted soybeans prevent penetration of the oil into the dough. This is desirable both because it improves the quality of the doughnuts and because it cuts down on oil consumption. But the reason why soybeans have the property has not yet been clearly explained.

Because of its foaming property, isolated soybean protein is used together with wheat flour in the preparation of sponge cakes, a Japanese honey cake called *Castella*, and cookies. But adjustments must be made in mixing time and amounts of water when it is used. For instance, to ensure the same texture as when it is not added, water must be increased because of isolated soy protein's high water absorption.

As a protein supplement
The United States Department of Agriculture has developed a product called CSM —largely for use in the developing nations—that consists of corn meal, defatted (or full-fat) soybeans, defatted milk, and oil. Intended to help people maintain a balanced diet, it can be processed in many way. For example, it can be mixed with water and heated to form a kind of porridge or it can be combined with other ingredients in confections and soups. The following is an example of the proportions of ingredients in CSM: 63.8 percent corn meal, 24.2 percent heat-treated defatted soybeans, and 5 percent defatted milk. In this case, CSM contains 19 percent protein. INCAPARINA, developed in the International Nutrition Center

of Central America and Panama, contains defatted or full-fat soybeans as a protein fortifier, taking the place of cottonseed flour used in a former similar mixture. To it is added food yeast and calcium carbonate. The Northern Regional Research Center of the United States Department of Agriculture has developed a readily digestible full-fat product by destroying lipoxygenase in whole soybeans by heating them directly and then extruding them to break down their tissues.

The most salient features of soybeans in their many nutritional applications are these: they can be combined with other ingredients and they do not lose nutritional value during processing. But, in devising ways to use them, adequate attention must be paid to nutritional, health and dietetic properties and to food habits or preferences of the country of region in question.

Other food uses of soy-protein products

One soybean product developed in Japan is made by soaking hulled, whole beans in water, heating them, and feeding them into a rotating stone to produce a substance with a threadlike texture. The simple process does not require removal of insoluble residue and whey. The resultant product can be used as an extender of meat and fish foods and in simulated meat products. At present in Japan research and experiments are being performed to develop still other products with characteristic functional properties from whole soybeans.

Part Two

Cooking with Soybean Food Products

Introduction

Soybeans

Like rice, wheat, and other grains, one single soybean is endowed with enough life and contains enough nourishment to germinate and produce a plant bearing many more beans just like itself. For centuries, the people of Japan have been aware of the nutritious wealth of these beans and have skillfully used them in daily diets. In the Japanese language, the very word *bean* (*mamè*) connotes mental and physical vigor and well-being. And at the Setsubun festival, held on February 3 or 4, toasted soybeans are tossed about the house and out the door to drive misfortune away and invite good fortune in. Sweet-cooked black soybeans are part of the standard New Year menu because eating them has traditionally been regarded as assurance of good health throughout the year. (Other indispensable elements of the New Year feast include *kazunoko* or herring roe, which is thought to guarantee the health of children and grandchidren and cooked sardines. The sardine was once used as fertilizer in rice fields and is included in the festive meal in the hope of abundant harvests of so-called Five Grains.)

Rice remains the staple of the Japanese diet. And, though it is a major source of protein, it is deficient in the necessary amino acid lysine, which cannot be produced naturally in the body. Other peoples obtain lysine from animal proteins in such foods as milk, eggs, meat and fish. But, though they have long been fond of fish, until fairly recent times, the Japanese people ate no eggs, dairy products, or meat. Buddhist influence tabooed the consumption of the flesh of quadrupeds like cows and pigs. The lysine deficiency was made up, however, by the inclusion of soybeans and soybean products in the rice-centered diet. As is unusual for vegetable proteins, soybeans are especially rich in lysine.

In addition to boiled and toasted soybeans, the Japanese consume large quantities of miso, tofu, *nattō*, and soy sauce. In these forms, the beans are easier to eat and more readily digestible. The standard Japanese meal centers on steamed rice and miso soup, a combination that is excellent from the nutritional standpoint, since the vegetable protein in the bean-paste soup compensates for the dietary insufficiencies of the rice. In other words, whereas people in the West turn to the animal proteins in cheese and butter to make up for the lysine lacking in the grains from which bread is made, the Japanese use soybeans to perform the same function in connection with rice.

In recent years, however, the high salt content of miso and soy sauce has been connected with the development of hypertension; and the Japanese now eat more meat, eggs, and dairy products than ever before in the past. Nonetheless, tofu and miso remain essential mainstays.

Soybeans are eaten in many different ways in various parts of Japan. Each region has its favorites and specialities. An unusual one is found in the northeast or Tōhoku region, where soybeans are soaked in water overnight and then flattened, individually, with a wooden mallet for faster cooking and easier eating. In the Yamagata district, these flattened beans are combined with carrot, *shiitake* mushrooms, devil's tongue jelly (*konnyaku*), and *abura-agè*; seasoned with soy sauce and sugar; and cooked till tender. Usually a large batch of this mixture is prepared in a big pot and then eaten cold with steamed rice as a convenient, nutritional standby for farmers in the busy agricultural season. Traditional since the Edo period (1603–1867), *hiyashi-jiru* always appears at weddings and funerals even today.

The people of Osaka prepare something called *jakko-mamè*, in which small river fish, like the roach, are grilled, dried, and then simmered together with soybeans. The people of the river regions of Ibaragi and Tochigi Prefectures prepare a dish called *sumitsukari*, in which toasted soybeans are simmered together with *daikon* radish, carrots, and *abura-agè* and flavored with sakè lees and vinegar. *Sumitsukari* from a house other than one's own is eaten on the first day of the ox in the year to prevent illness. In other districts, soybeans are steamed together with glutinous rice, ground to a powder, and prepared in many different ways.

Soybeans must be soaked in three or four times their volume of water before cooking. Since the beans expand, a large container is necessary. The soaking time is from six to eight hours in winter and from five to six hours in summer. Water absorption causes the beans to swell from 2.5 to 3.5 times their dry volume. Absorption is complete in from six to eight hours; after this time, beans will absorb no more water.

After soaking, the beans are put on the heat in the water in which they have stood. A deep, heavy kettle with good insulating properties is best. Water evaporates too quickly from a shallow pan. Cover the kettle, and bring the contents to a boil over a high heat. Then regulate the heat to ensure a quiet, rolling simmer. New beans cook faster than old ones; but, in general from three to four hours of gentle simmering is required. Make certain the beans remain submerged by a depth of two centimeters, adding hot water as necessary during the cooking process. Because of their high protein content, soybeans boil over easily. Caution is required on this point.

The beans are done when pressure applied by thumb and middle finger will squash one. The human hand is capable of exerting more pressure with the thumb and index finger than with the thumb and middle finger and more with the thumb and middle finger than with the thumb and little finger. Beans that flatten readily between the thumb and index finger are still underdone. Beans that flatten between the thumb and little finger are extra tender, as they must be in the production of miso.

Seasoning must not be done till the beans are tender. Added too soon, flavorings toughen the beans. For ordinary purposes, soy sauce and sugar may be added after one hour's simmering. In the preparation of sweet bean dishes, however, sugar must not be added till the beans are completely tender. Even then, it must not be added all at once, as this raises the concentration of the simmering stock, thus drawing moisture from the beans and either making them tough or causing them to wrinkle. If sugar is added in two or three parts, the beans will be tender and as smooth-skinned as grapes.

A pressure cooker may be used when beans must be prepared in a hurry. The beans must still be soaked in water. When the steam has built up in the cooker, simmer over a low heat for about ten minutes. Remove from the heat, open the valve to release the steam, and allow the cooker to cool completely before opening. An inner perforated plate is essential to prevent the beans from clogging the valve during cooking.

To conserve on energy, soaked soybeans may be combined with hot water in a thermos bottle and allowed to stand for a day. They will then be tender and may be seasoned and finished in a kettle on the stove.

It takes little more time or trouble to prepare a large batch of simmered beans, which may then be packaged in serving portions and frozen. At cooking time, the frozen beans may be placed, unthawed, in a pan, heated, and seasoned to taste.

Using tofu and tofu products

Tofu is loved by people of all ages and stations for the versatility that makes it at home on all occasions. At a certain temple in Kyoto is a plaque bearing the following inscription, which, while comparing this food to religious faith, clearly shows the esteem in which the Japanese people hold tofu.

"Religious faith should be like tofu: it is good under any circumstances. It is good boiled, grilled, or fried. Raw, chilled, served with soy sauce and other seasonings, it is good with steamed rice. Simmered in hot water and flavored, it is good with sakè. Because it is soft, old people and sick people welcome it, but children and young people like it too. Men like it, women like it; poor and rich both like it. Though common, it has elegance enough to find a place in the upper class.

"It cuts clean and well for use in clear broths. It is good in the meatless diets of religious training. It can be crushed for use in miso soup.

"It is used all the time and in all seasons. It is inexpensive yet numbered among the delicious treats. It is welcomed everywhere, in mountains as well as in big cities. It is well received at dinners for dignitaries and guests yet is convenient enough for college students who do their own cooking.

"Women especially should be like tofu. The mature and cultivated person should be tender, yet firm, like tofu. Though apparently tasteless, it is delicious. Though apparently ordinary, it is extraordinary."

In Japan, if a person is at a loss for an extra ingredient to put in the miso soup, there is always tofu, which everyone welcomes. For the several varieties of tofu—toasted tofu, *abura-agè*, *nama-agè*, *gammodoki*, dried-frozen tofu, and so on—please see Part I.

The name of an Edo-period book called *One-hundred Tofu Delicacies* gives an idea of the multitude of ways in which this product can be prepared. Actually, however, with the addition of modern and Chinese methods, the number of dishes made from tofu probably rises to about five hundred. The simplest way to eat it is merely to cut it into bite-size pieces and serve it—chilled in summer (*hiya-yakko*) or heated in hot water in winter (*yu-dōfu*)—with a dip of soy sauce flavored in various ways. In the Gifu region, prepared mustard is added to the soy sauce. More generally it is flavored with chopped scallion, shaved dried bonito, or grated ginger root.

For use in miso soup or clear broth, tofu may be cut into small dice; thin rectangular slices; or sometimes long, thin strips. There are about thirty ways to cut tofu for soup. Or it may be crumbled in the hands and added to the liquid. This method is preferred by some because no knife, which is thought to spoil the flavor of the tofu, is called into play. Crumbled tofu is sometimes sautéed in oil and served in a light broth flavored with soy sauce and salt.

In all but a few exceptional instances, tofu must not be overheated, or it toughens. For instance, when the hot water for *yu-dōfu* boils and the tofu begins to move gently, it is done and must be eaten at once. In the case of miso soup, the tofu should be added after the bean paste has been dissolved; and the soup should be served as soon as it has reached the boiling point.

For fried and deep-fried foods, regular or cotton tofu is used and must be drained. There are several ways to do this. The tofu may be dropped gently into hot water then drained in a colander. Or it may be wrapped in a kitchen towel, placed on a chopping board, and topped with another chopping board (or plate), which serves as a weight to press out moisture. The bottom chopping board should be raised at one end to facilitate drainage.

Delicate and easily broken, in shops where it is prepared, tofu is floated in water for cutting. In the home, you should place the block of tofu on the palm of the left hand and make vertical and horizontal incisions in it with a knife held in the right. (See illustration on next page.) Jar lids or special cutters may be used to make round pieces.

Fried tofu products, like *abura-agè* and *nama-agè*, are usually treated to remove some of the oil remaining in them from the frying process. Either put them in a colander and pour boiling water over them or dip them briefly in a kettle of boiling water. Removing the oil kills offensive odors and prevents unpleasant greasy slicks on the finished food.

Abura-agè takes the form of closed pouches, which must be opened for the preparation of such dishes as *inari-zushi*. To make separating the layers easier, place the *abura-agè* on a flat surface and roll either chopsticks or a rolling pin over it lightly.

Tofu and *abura-agè* should be stored in the refrigerator. Put tofu in a container of water. It will last two or three days if the water is changed daily. Aseptic-packed tofu will keep for about a week if the seal remains unbroken. Because of its high moisture content, tofu cannot be frozen without altering its texture, though it is possible to freeze *abura-agè*, *nama-agè*, and *gammodoki*. Some Japanese housewives deliberately freeze tofu, however, to make something like the product known as dried-frozen tofu, which, though spongy instead of smooth, absorbs seasoning flavors well and has a special tastiness of its own.

Cutting Tofu

Yakko or eight cubes
Cut vertically in half and horizontally in quarters.

Square slices (*Shikishi*)
Cut vertically in half. Then cut crosswise at intervals of ⅛ in (5 mm).

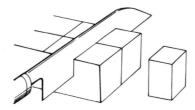

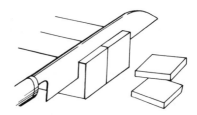

Dice
Cut the block of tofu horizontally in half or thirds. Then cut it vertically at intervals equal to widths of the horizontal slices to make small (⅜ in or 1 cm) cubes. Smaller cubes may be cut in a similar fashion.

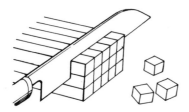

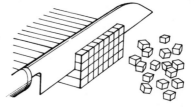

Rectangular slices (*Tanzaku*)
Cut vertically in half then horizontally in half. Then cut crosswise at intervals of ⅛ in (5 mm).

Rectangular blocks (*Hyōshigi*)
Cut vertically in half and horizontally into thirds. Then cut crosswise at intervals of ⅜ in (1 cm).

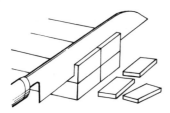

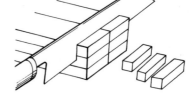

Chrysanthemum cut
Cut horizontally and vertically at intervals of ⅛ in (5 mm), leaving ⅜ in (1 cm) uncut at one end.

Mince

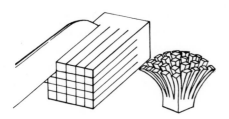

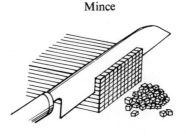

Nattō *and* kinako

In Tokyo in the past, street vendors went from house to house selling *nattō*. The kind of *nattō* that makes strings when the beans are separated from each other is popular in the north of the Kanto region. Ordinarily, *nattō* is eaten with steamed rice and are flavored with soy sauce. Sometimes fine crushed *nori* seaweed, shaved, dried bonito, chopped scallion, or raw egg yolk is mixed with *nattō*.

Nattō may be pounded in a mortar and used as a coating for other foods. It is sometimes served with squid or tuna or with boiled flat chives (*nira*) or the root called *yamaimo*. In recent years, it has become popular to sauté *nattō* or use it in tempura. The *Bacillus nattō* in this product contains enzymes that stimulate the digestion. *Nattō* will keep for about a week in the refrigerator and may be frozen.

Mixed with sugar, the toasted soy flour called *kinako* is eaten with plain steamed rice, on rice balls, on dumplings made of wheat flour, or on a jelly like desert made from arrowroot starch; but its most popular use is as a coating for toasted glutinous rice cake (*mochi*) that has been dipped in hot water. Since moisture spoils it, *kinako* should be kept in an airtight container.

Tofu

Homemade Tofu

Tofu may be made by soaking the beans in water and then grinding them in a blender or by first pulverizing the beans. In either case, after cooking, calcium sulfate should be used as a coagulating agent since it is more readily obtainable than the natural substance called *nigari* used for this purpose in Japan. The coagulating agent is added at a rate of from 0.5 to 1 percent of the volume of the soy milk. The smaller the amount, the more delicious the tofu.

> **1 lb (450 g) soybeans**
> **calcium sulfate (from 0.5 to 1 % volume of soy milk)**

Method I (*the beans are soaked in water*)
 1.   Wash the beans. Cover them with ample water and allow them to stand for eitht hours in the summer or fifteen hours in the winter, or until the beans have doubled in bulk.
 2.   Put the beans and their soaking water (add water if too much of it has been absorbed by the beans) in a blender and blend for two or three minutes.
 3.   In a large container put about ten times as much water as the volume of the beans. Add the blended beans; bring to a boil, taking care the mixture does not boil over; then reduce the heat to low and simmer, stirring constantly, for fifteen minutes.

4. Strain the mixture through a cloth bag. The resulting white liquid is soy milk. The residue is called *okara*.

5. Dissolve the calcium sulfate in ¾ cup water. Cool the soy milk to about 158°F (70°C) and add half of the calcium-sulfate mixture. Stir well to prevent the coagulating agent's forming sediment. Stand the container of soy milk in a larger container filled with water at about 178°F (80°C). Add the remaining coagulating agent and allow the mixture to stand for about fifteen minutes. The bean protein will set, forming curds that float to the surface. Additions of calcium sulfate must be made at a temperature of 158°F (70°C).

6. Spread cotton cloth in a deep colander. Scoop the curds into the colander. When all curds have been collected, weight them lightly and allow them to drain for ten minutes. If you wish to make the usual rectangular blocks of tofu, perforate the bottoms and sides of wooden or plastic boxes, line them with cloth, and use them in place of the colander. If curds do not form and set, add a little more calcium sulfate. The weight used in the draining process must not be too heavy as this makes the tofu tough.

Method II (the beans are ground first)

1. Grind the beans in a blender or coffee mill. Add about 2 qt (2 l) of water and allow the mixture to stand for approximately thirty minutes.

2. When the beans have absorbed the water, add to them from 4 to 5 qt (from 4 to 5 l) of boiling water in a large kettle. Reduce the heat to low and simmer for about twenty minutes, taking care the mixture neither scorches nor boils over.

3. Strain the mixture through cloth to produce soy milk and proceed according to the preceding recipe.

Makes four blocks (2⅘ lbs or about 1.2 k) of tofu.

Note: In Japan an instant tofu product is marketed. To produce it, soy milk is frozen and then powdered. The homemaker dissolves this powder in water, brings the mixture to a boil, adds the coagulating agent (*nigari*) included in the package, and allows it to set. Sometimes minced parsley or *shiso* or even chopped ham is added to the mixture. Enough to make two standard blocks of tofu sells for one hundred yen.

Kenchin Soup

A very warming dish for a cold winter night.

> **1 block tofu**
> **½ stalk burdock (*gobō*)**
> **1 segment 8 in (20 cm) *daikon* radish**
> **5 or 6 taros**
> **1 small carrot**
> **1 block *konnyaku* (devil's tongue jelly)**

      sesame oil
      1½ or 2 tsp salt
      1 tsp sakè
      1–2 Tbsp soy sauce
      dash of monosodium glutamate
      minced scallion

1.   Wrap the tofu in a clean kitchen towel and squeeze out as much moisture as possible.

2.   Scrape the burdock then shave it into fine flakes, as if you were sharpening a pencil. Remove astringency by allowing the burdock to stand in freshwater.

3.   Peel the section of *daikon* radish. Slice it into rounds ⅛ in (5 mm) thick then quarter these. Peel the taros. Slice them into rounds ¾ in (2 cm) thick. Soak the slices in water to remove astringency. Peel the carrot, cut it into rounds ⅛ in (5 mm) thick, and quarter the rounds. Cut the cake of *konnyaku* vertically in half then slice the resulting strips into slices ¾ in (2 cm) wide.

4.   Over a medium heat in a deep pot heat sesame oil. In the oil sauté first the tofu. Then add the vegetables and the *konnyaku* in that order. Add four cups of boiling water. Lower the heat and simmer for a while.

5.   When the vegetables are half done, season the soup with salt, sakè, soy sauce, and monosodium glutamate. Continue simmering till the vegetables are tender. Before serving, sprinkle with minced scallions.

Severs four.

Tofu and *Shiitake*-mushroom Soup

Little seasoning is necessary since the delectable flavor of the soup is produced by the principal ingredients themselves.

      1 block tofu
      4 medium dried *shiitake* mushrooms
      1 small boiled bamboo shoot
      4 cups good chicken stock
      pinch of salt
      small amount soy sauce

1.   Cut the tofu into thin bite-size pieces.

2.   Soften the *shiitake* mushrooms by allowing them to stand in lukewarm water. Remove and discard the stems. Press out as much moisture as possible and slice the caps in half.

3.   Cut the bamboo shoot into thin bite-size pieces.

4.   In a saucepan bring the chicken stock to a boil, add the dried mushrooms. Reduce the heat to low, and simmer. Next add the bamboo shoot and tofu and

simmer for a while. Taste and correct the seasoning with salt and soy sauce if necessary. Bring to a boil again then remove from heat.

Serves four.

Note: The flavor is enhanced if the water in which the *shiitake* mushrooms were soaked is added to the stock. Shrimp, crab, and chicken meat may be added.

Tofu and Chopped-chicken Soup

  1 block regular tofu
  3½ oz (100 g) boned, skinned chicken breasts
  2 Tbsp sakè
  ¼ egg white
  1 Tbsp cornstarch (traditionally starch made from the dogtooth violet)
  4 cups good chicken stock
  pinch of salt
  small amount lard
  small amount chopped parsley

  1.   Boil the tofu briefly in two cups water. Drain and pound in a mortar or run through a food processor.
  2.   Remove tendons from chicken breasts. Chop them fine then pound them in a mortar or run them through a food processor. Season with sakè and add lightly beaten egg white.
  3.   Combine tofu and chicken breasts. Combine with this mixture 1 Tbsp cornstarch dissolved in 2 Tbsp water.
  4.   In a saucepan bring the chicken stock to a boil and season it with salt.
  5.   Gently pour the tofu and chicken mixture into the boiling soup. Reduce the heat to low. When the chicken meat surfaces, add the lard. Remove from the heat. It is important not to overcook the soup. Serve sprinkled with chopped parsley.

Serves four.

Chilled Savory Tofu (*Hiya-yakko*)

The tofu should be well chilled for this simple, but perennially popular dish.

  2 blocks tofu
  2 tsp salt
  ¾ cup light stock
  5 Tbsp soy sauce
  4 Tbsp *mirin* sweetened saké
  ⅓ cucumber
  1 small radish

ice

Choice of seasonings and garnishes including any or all of the following: minced scallion, chopped green *shiso* leaves, pitted salted plums, shaved dried bonito, *shichimi* seven-spice powder, and so on.

1. Bring five cups of water seasoned with 2 tsp salt to a boil. Cut tofu into fairly large cubes. Lower them gently into hot water, which must not be allowed to boil again once the tofu is added. Remove after a few minutes, drain, and chill in the refrigerator.

2. Combine stock, soy sauce, and *mirin* in a saucepan. Bring to a boil then remove from heat at once and cool.

3. Salt the cucumber. Roll it on a board to wilt it slightly. Slice it into thin rounds.

4. Slice the radish into thin rounds.

5. Partly fill a deep serving dish with cold water. Add some ice and the cut chilled tofu. Float the cucumber and radish slices on the water. Provide each diner with a small bowl of the cooled stock and soy sauce mixture. Arrange all the seasonings and garnishes conveniently. Each person flavors his sauce as he likes and dips pieces of chilled tofu in it before eating them.

Serves four.

Chilled Tofu and Fish

2 blocks tofu
4 slices fish (cod, sea bream, or similar white-flesh fish)
pinch of salt
small amount sakè
small amound cornstarch (traditionally starch made from the dogtooth violet)
6 cups light stock
1 cucumber
4 fresh *shiitake* mushrooms
1 scallion
1 tomato
4 green *shiso* leaves
$1\frac{1}{2}$ tsp salt
small amount soy sauce
1 lemon

1. After allowing the tofu to stand in salted water for a little while, heat it briefly in four cups of boiling water. Drain and cut into fairly large cubes.

2. Slice the fish thin and sprinkle it with salt and sakè. Coat each slice with cornstarch. Bring two cups of stock to a boil and briefly cook the fish slices in it.

3. Sprinkle the cucumber with salt and roll it on a board to wilt it slightly. Slice it into thin rounds. Add a little more salt to the stock in which the fish was boiled and parboil the cucumber slices in it.

4.   Remove and discard the stems of the *shiitake* mushrooms. Parboil the caps in one cup water. Mince the scallion and allow it to stand in cold water.

5.   Slice the tomato into thin rounds then halve each round.

6.   Wash green *shiso* leaves and spread them in the bottom of a serving bowl. On top of the leaves attractively arrange the tofu, fish slices, cucumber, *shiitake* mushrooms, and tomato slices. Chill in the refrigerator.

7.   Prepare a sauce by boiling four cups of light stock seasoned with 1½ tsp salt. Chill this sauce. Sprinkle the ingredients with the sauce before serving. Each diner should be provided with a small dish and soy sauce into which to dip the individual pieces from the bowl. Garnish with minced scallion and lemon wedges.

Serves four.

Steamed-tofu Rolls

> 1 block regular tofu
> small amount flour
> small amount sugar
> small amount salt
> 1 oz (30 g) carrot
> 1 cup light stock
> 1 tsp sakè
> 1 tsp soy sauce
> 1½ tsp salt
> ½ tsp sugar
> 1¾ oz (50 g) spinach
> 2 sheets dried laver (*nori*)

1.   Lightly drain the tofu. Pound it in a mortar or run it through a food processor. Mix flour with it. Wrap this mixture in a clean kitchen towel and steam it in the top part of a steamer for from fifteen to twenty minutes.

2.   Pound the tofu again and flavor it with sugar and salt to taste.

3.   Cut the carrot into fine julienne strips. Bring one cup of stock flavored with sakè, soy sauce, salt, and sugar to a boil in a saucepan. Add the carrot and cook till tender over a medium heat.

4.   Wash spinach. Parboil it in hot salted water. Remove before the color changes and plunge in cold water. Squeeze out as much water as possible.

5.   Spread one sheet of laver (*nori*) on a bamboo rolling mat. On top of this, leaving the far edge of the *nori* open, spread half of the pounded and steamed tofu. Along the center of the tofu, make a neat strip of carrot. Roll the *nori* with the fillings to make a neat, fairly firm roll. Remove the bamboo mat. Repeat with the remaining half of the tofu, replacing the carrot with spinach.

6.   Using a sharp knife, cut the rolls into serving pieces. Season the spinach rolls with a few drops of soy sauce.

Serves four.

Tofu in Chicken Sauce

1–1½ blocks tofu
6 cups light stock
3½ oz (100 g) ground chicken meat
½ cup soy sauce
1½ tsp salt
2 tsp cornstarch
citron rind or grated ginger

1. Drain the tofu, weighted, to reduce water content. Cut it into fairly large slices.
2. In a saucepan combine stock and chicken meat. Bring to a boil and simmer till the meat is done, removing all scum that floats to the surface.
3. Add soy sauce and salt to the saucepan and bring to a boil again.
4. Dissolve the cornstarch in 4 tsp of water. Add to the pan and simmer till the sauce is clear and thick. Add the tofu and simmer briefly over a low heat.
5. Put slices of tofu in individual serving dishes, coat generously with the sauce, and garnish with either slivers of citron rind or small mounds of grated ginger.

Serves four.

Tofu Family Casserole (*Yu-dōfu*)

3 blocks tofu
7 oz (200 g) *daikon* radish
2 scallions
½ lemon
1 small piece fresh ginger root
small amount *wasabi* horseradish
1 sheet dried laver (*nori*)
1 cup flaked dried bonito (*katsuobushi*)
8 in (20 cm) kelp (*kombu*)
½ cup soy sauce
1 Tbsp sweetened sakè (*mirin*)

1. Divide the thickness of the cakes of tofu in half. Then make two longitudinal and three crosswise incisions to cut each block into twelve cubes.
2. Peel and grate the *daikon* radish. Mince the scallions. Cut the lemon into wedges. Peel and grate the ginger root. If you are using fresh *wasabi* horseradish, peel and grate it. If you are using powder, prepare it according to directions. If prepared tubed *wasabi* is available, it may be used as it is. Convenient dried bonito flakes are sold packaged.

3.   Though it may be prepared on the stove and carried to the table, this dish is more fun to cook and eat if everything but the basic preparations is done on a heating source before the diners. Partly fill with water a large casserole or other heatproof container that may be brought to the table. Allow the kelp to stand in this water a while. Then over a low heat, bring the water to a boil. Combine the soy sauce and *mirin* in a smaller heatproof container and stand it in the center of the casserole of water.

4.   Gently lower the tofu into the hot water and continue to simmer it. Each guest should be provided with a small container for soy sauce and the condiments of his choice. As the tofu is heated through, the diners pick up bits and dip them into the seasoned soy sauce before eating them.

Serves four.

Tofu and Egg Casserole

> **2 blocks silken tofu**
> **¹⁄₂ scallion**
> **1¹⁄₂ cups light stock**
> **2 Tbsp sweetened sakè (*mirin*)**
> **2 Tbsp soy sauce**
> **1 Tbsp sakè**
> **¹⁄₄ tsp salt**
> **3 eggs**
> **chopped trefoil (*mitsuba*)**

1.   Cut the tofu into long, narrow strips ¾ in (2 cm) thick. Allow the strips to soak in water.

2.   Cut the scallion into strips 1–1½ in (3–4 cm) long then split these vertically into four equal parts.

3.   In a saucepan combine stock, *mirin*, soy sauce, sakè, and salt. Bring to a boil.

4.   Gently lower the tofu strips into the pot. When the tofu begins to move gently, sprinkle the scallion strips on top. Lightly beat the three eggs and pour them on top of the mixture in the pan. Simmer over a low heat till the eggs are half set. Remove from the heat.

5.   Gently divide the contents of the pan among four individual serving dishes. Garnish with coarsely chopped trefoil. A lighter version of this dish may be prepared in a similar way, but omitting the eggs. Dried bonito flakes and a garnish of scallions that have been refreshed by a soaking in cold water enhance the flavor.

Serves four.

Tofu and Fried Fish in Clear Sauce

> **2 blocks tofu**
> **2 slices white-flesh fish (flounder or cod)**
> **2 tsp fresh ginger-root juice**
> **2 tsp soy sauce**
> **2 tsp sakè**
> **pinch of salt**
> **1 small piece fresh ginger root**
> **$\frac{1}{2}$ scallion**
> **1 egg white**
> **2 Tbsp cornstarch**
> **oil for frying**
> **1 Tbsp salad oil**
> **$\frac{1}{2}$ Tbsp soy sauce**
> **1 cup light stock**
> **$\frac{2}{3}$ tsp salt**
> **$\frac{1}{2}$ Tbsp cornstarch**
> **2 Tbsp green peas**

1. Cut each block of tofu vertically in half then slice it diagonally into pieces $\frac{3}{8}$ in (1 cm) thick.
2. Cut the fish into bite-size slices. Sprinkle them with ginger juice, soy sauce, sakè, and a pinch of salt and allow them to stand for twenty minutes.
3. Peel the ginger root and slice it into thin rounds. Coarsely chop the scallion.
4. Lightly beat the egg white; do not allow it to foam. Dip each piece of fish first into the egg white and then into cornstarch.
5. Heat frying oil to 340°F (170°C). Fry the fish pieces till crisp and done. Remove from oil and drain.
6. In a large frying pan—a Chinese *wok* is best—heat the salad oil. Sauté in it first the slices of ginger then the scallion. To the frying pan add soy sauce, stock, and salt. Dissolve the cornstarch in 1 Tbsp water and add it to the pan. When the sauce is thick and clear, add the tofu and green peas. When these ingredients are heated through, add the fried fish. Serve at one.

Serves four.

Braised Tomatoes and Tofu

> **2 blocks tofu**
> **7 oz (200 g) thin sliced pork**
> **2 tsp sakè**
> **2 tsp soy sauce**
> **1 tomato**
> **2 Tbsp salad oil**

2 Tbsp soy sauce
1 tsp red-pepper oil (*ra-yu*)
dash of pepper
chopped parsley

1.   Cut the tofu into moderately large cubes and allow it to drain for a while in a colander.

2.   Cut the pork into slices 2 in (5 cm) long and marinate the slices in sakè and soy sauce.

3.   Cut the tomato into eight wedges.

4.   In a large frying pan—a Chinese *wok* is best—heat salad oil. Sauté the pork till it changes color. Add the tofu, tomato, soy sauce, red-pepper oil, and pepper.

5.   When the ingredients are almost done add ½ cup hot water.

6.   Transfer the ingredients to an earthenware casserole or other casserole that can be brought to the table. Bring to a boil, sprinkle with chopped parsley, and serve at once.

Serves four.

Tofu Variety Casserole

2 blocks tofu
3½ oz (100 g) chicken meat
6 dried shrimp
1 Tbsp sakè
2 fresh *shiitake* mushrooms
3½ oz (100 g) boiled bamboo shoot
1¾ oz (50 g) spinach
2 scallops
2 cup chicken stock
½ Tbsp salt
1 Tbsp soy sauce
small amount lard

1.   Cut the tofu into bite-size cubes.

2.   Cut the chicken into cubes 1¾ in (3 cm) to a side and parboil them briefly in two cups boiling water.

3.   Wash the dried shrimp and marinate them in sakè.

4.   Remove and discard the stems of the mushrooms. Cut the caps into thin strips. Cut the boiled bamboo shoot into thin slices.

5.   Briefly boil the spinach in three cups of salted water. Do not allow it to change color. Remove it and plunge it at once into cold water. Squeeze out as much moisture as possible and cut the spinach into segments 2 in (5 cm) long.

6.   Allow the scallops to stand for a while in lightly salted water.

7.   In an earthenware casserole or large pot combine stock, salt, soy sauce,

and all the other ingredients except the spinach. Simmer over a low heat till the contents are heated through. Raise the heat and bring the contents to a boil then reduce the heat to low again and simmer for thirty minutes. Add the spinach and lard immediately before serving.

Serves four.

Skewered Tofu (*Dengaku*)

> **2 blocks regular tofu**
> **heavy bamboo skewers**
> *Topping A:*
> > **1 cup mild miso (*ama*-miso)**
> > **3 Tbsp sweetened sakè (*mirin*)**
> > **1 cup light stock**
> > **½ cup sugar**
> > ***sanshō* pepper powder**
> *Topping B:*
> > **7 oz (200 g) or 1 cup light miso (*shiro*-miso)**
> > **3 Tbsp (or slightly less) sweetened sakè (*mirin*)**
> > **slightly less than ½ cup sugar**
> > **1 egg yolk**
> > **prepared mustard**
> > ***kinomè***

1. Press out moisture from the blocks of tofu in the following way. Wrap the tofu in a clean, dry cloth. Place it on a chopping board. Weight it with another chopping board and prop one end of the bottom up slightly to create an incline along which water can flow. Allow the tofu to stand this way for about thirty minutes. Flat plates may be used in place of chopping boards, and a kettle of water may be placed on the upper plate as a weight.

2. Prepare topping A by combining in a saucepan miso, *mirin*, stock, and sugar. Stirring constantly to prevent scorching, cook over a low heat till the sugar has melted and a smooth paste forms. Divide the paste in two and mix the *sanshō* pepper powder with one half.

3. Prepare topping B in the same way as topping A. Divide the paste in half. Pound the *kinomè* leaves in a mortar and mix them with half of the paste. Combine the remaining half with the egg yolk and cook over a low heat till thick and smooth.

4. Cut the tofu crosswise in slices ⅜ in (1 cm) thick. Skewer each piece on a heavy bamboo skewer. The ones traditionally used for this dish are wide, flat, and double-pronged. An open charcoal fire or a grill that can be placed directly over an open flame is needed to toast the tofu. Dry the tofu over a high heat; hold the tofu well away from the flame. Top the skewered tofu with some of each of the four toppings. Toast the tofu—uncoated side down—until the underside is slightly

browned. Garnish the topping-A tofu with mustard and the remainder with *kinomè* leaves.

Serves four,

Grilled Tofu

> **2 blocks tofu**
> **1 heaping Tbsp white sesame seeds**
> **2 Tbsp minced scallion**
> **1 tsp crushed garlic**
> **½ tsp minced ginger**
> **1½ Tbsp soy sauce**
> **1 Tbsp sugar**
> **small amount sesame oil**

1.   Cut the tofu crosswise in slices ⅜ in (1 cm) thick. Wrap them in a clean, dry cloth and let them drain, weighted, on a tilted board for from thirty minutes to an hour.
2.   Toast the sesame seeds and pound them in a mortar or grind them in a blender.
3.   In a bowl combine scallions, garlic, ginger, sesame seeds, soy sauce, sugar, and sesame oil to make a marinade.
4.   Allow the tofu slices to marinate in this mixture for a few minutes. On a wire grill over a charcoal or other open fire, toast the tofu till it is browned and heated through. Brush on additional marinade from time to time during the grilling and take care not to let the sauce burn.

Serves four.

Tofu *au Gratin*

> **2 blocks regular tofu**
> **salt**
> **pepper**
> **2 thin slices bacon**
> **¼ onion**
> **1 Tbsp salad oil**
> **1 Tbsp butter**
> **3 eggs**
> **2 cups milk**
> **½ cup cream**
> **1 tsp salt**
> **dash of nutmeg**
> **½ cup grated cheese**

1.   Allow the tofu to drain, wrapped in a clean, dry cloth, for a few minutes. Cut crosswise in slices ⅜ in (1 cm) thick. Sprinkle with salt and pepper.

2.   Mince bacon and onion.

3.   Heat salad oil in a frying pan and sauté the bacon and onion in it. Add butter and tofu.

4.   When the butter is melted, arrange the tofu slices in an ovenproof casserole or in individual ovenproof serving dishes. Top with the minced onion and bacon bits.

5.   In a bowl, mix the lightly beaten eggs, milk, cream, salt, and nutmeg. Strain this mixture.

6.   Pour the egg mixture over the tofu. Top with grated cheeese and bake in an oven, heated to 400°F (205°C), for forty minutes.

Serves four.

Tofu Omelet (*Gisei-dōfu*)

> 2 blocks regular tofu
> ½ carrot
> 2 fresh *shiitake* mushrooms
> ⅔ oz (20 g) string beans
> 1 Tbsp salad oil
> 4 Tbsp sugar
> 1 tsp salt
> 1 Tbsp soy sauce
> dash of monosodium glutamate
> 2 eggs

1.   Crumble the tofu and boil it for from two to three minutes in five cups of water. Spread a kitchen towel in a colander and drain the tofu in this. Reducing the amount of water in the tofu determines the success of this dish.

2.   Peel the carrot and cut it into julienne strips about 1–1½ in (3–4 cm) long. Remove and discard the stems of the *shiitake* mushrooms. Julienne cut the caps.

3.   String the beans and cut them into fine diagonal strips. Parboil them for a few minutes in one cup of boiling water and drain.

4.   Heat 1 Tbsp of salad oil in a frying pan. In it sauté the carrot, *shiitake* mushroom, and tofu. Add sugar, salt, soy sauce, and monosodium glutamate,

5.   Beat the eggs. Remove the frying pan from the heat and stir in the eggs.

6.   For the final frying it is best to use the rectangular Japanese pan designed for thick omelets. Oil such a pan with butter and salad oil and heat it thoroughly. Pour in the tofu mixture. Cook over a medium heat till one side is done. Turn and continue cooking till firm. Remove from the pan and cut into serving pieces.

Serves four,

Unohana

This dish makes use of the pulp (*unohana* or *okara*) left after the soy milk necessary for the production of tofu has been prepared. It is inexpensive and nutritious.

> **2 cups soy pulp (*unohana*)**
> **1 small squid**
> **dash of salt**
> **small amount sakè**
> **5–6 Jew's ears (*kikuragè*)**
> **½ small carrot**
> **⅓ small stalk burdock root (*gobō*)**
> **½ small *asatsuki* scallion (optional)**
> **2 Tbsp salad oil**
> **1 cup light stock**
> **1 egg**
> **2 Tbsp sugar**
> **2 Tbsp sweetened sakè (*mirin*)**
> **1 Tbsp soy sauce**
> **2 tsp salt**
> **small amount vinegar**

1. Clean, open, and skin the squid. Sprinkle it with salt and sakè and allow it to stand for fifteen minutes. Grill it on a wire mat over an open flame. Cut the body into thin strips ¾ in (2 cm) long. Cut the legs into strips from ¾ to 1 in (from 2 to 3 cm) long.
2. Soften the Jew's ears in warm water then julienne cut them.
3. Peel the carrot and cut it into julienne strips ¾ in (2 cm) long. Scrape the burdock root. Cut it into julienne strips ¾ in (2 cm) long and allow them to stand in vinegared water for a while to remove astringency. Slice the *asatsuki* scallion fine.
4. Heat oil in a frying pan. Sauté the carrot and burdock root briefly. Add the *asatsuki* scallion.
5. Add the soy pulp, squid, Jew's ear, stock, and lightly beaten egg. Mix well. Season with sugar, *mirin*, soy sauce, salt, and vinegar. Stirring constantly with a fork to prevent scorching, continue cooking over a moderate heat till all liquid has evaporated and a fluffy, soft texture forms.

Serves four.

Scrambled Tofu (*Iri-dōfu*)

> **2 blocks tofu**
> **1⅖ oz (40 g) carrot**

4 fresh *shiitake* mushrooms
⅔ oz (20 g) snow peas
small amount sugar
pinch of salt
1 Tbsp salad oil
2 Tbsp sugar
2½ Tbsp soy sauce

1. Crumble the tofu in a saucepan. Add two cups water and bring to a boil. Then drain in a colander lined with a clean kitchen towel.
2. Peel carrot. Remove and discard stems of *shiitake* mushrooms. Cut both into short julienne strips.
3. Parboil the snow peas in one cup of hot water. Drain. In a saucepan combine one cup water and small amounts of sugar and salt. Briefly boil the snow peas again in this liquid. Drain and cut into julienne strips.
4. In a large frying pan—preferably a Chinese *wok*—heat salad oil. Sauté first the *shiitake* mushrooms. Then add the carrot. Next add the drained tofu. Stirring constantly, cook till all liquid has evaporated. Season with sugar and soy sauce and continue cooking a few more minutes.
5. Heap in individual serving dishes and top with julienne-cut snow peas.

Serves four.

Thunderous Tofu (*Kaminari-dōfu*)

The surprising name derives from the sound the tofu makes when it is sautéed.

1 block tofu
½ bunch spinach
2 Tbsp dried shrimp
2 Tbsp salad oil
2 Tbsp soy sauce
1 Tbsp sugar
1 tsp pepper oil (*ra-yu*)
pinch of salt

1. Wrap the tofu in a large, clean, dry kitchen towel. Squeeze out as much moisture as possible. Then, without removing the towel, crumble the tofu fine.
2. Briefly boil the spinach in five cups of salted water. Plunge in cold water, squeeze out as much moisture as possible, and cut in convenient lengths.
3. Soften the dried shrimp in a half cup water.
4. In a large frying pan—preferably a Chinese *wok*—heat oil well. Sprinkle the tofu in the oil. Stir till it is fine in texture.
5. Spread the spinach in a serving dish. Top this with tofu. Sprinkle the dried shrimp on the tofu.

6. Combine soy sauce, sugar, pepper oil, and salt, Pour over the tofu.

Serves four.

Tofu Topped with Meat

    2 blocks tofu
    2 Tbsp white sesame seeds
    5¼ oz (150 g) ground pork
    2 Tbsp minced scallion
    2 Tbsp sesame oil
    1½ Tbsp soy sauce
    small amount crushed garlic
    dash of pepper
    small amount powdered red pepper
    1 sheet dried laver (*nori*)
    2 Tbsp salad oil

1. Wrap the tofu in clean kitchen towels and allow it to drain in a colander lightly weighted for thirty minutes. Then cut it into bite-size pieces half the thickness of a full block.
2. Toast the sesame seeds then pound them in a mortar or grind them in blender.
3. In a bowl combine ground pork, minced scallions, sesame seeds, sesame oil, soy sauce, garlic, pepper, and red pepper. Blend well with your hands till the mixture coheres.
4. Top each piece of tofu with a piece of *nori* cut to fit perfectly. Spread a little of the pork mixture evenly on top of the *nori*.
5. Heat salad oil in a frying pan. Fry the pieces, tofu side first, on both sides. Allow the pork-mixture side to cook a little longer.

Serves four.

Sautéed Tofu and Champignons

    1 block regular tofu
    1¾ oz (50 g) champignons
    ⅓ scallion
    1 small piece fresh ginger root
    1¾ oz (50 g) green peas
    2 Tbsp salad oil
    5 Tbsp stock
    slightly less than 4 Tbsp oyster sauce
    ½–⅔ Tbsp soy sauce
    2 Tbsp sakè

dash of pepper
1 Tbsp cornstarch

1.   Dip the tofu in three cups boiling water. Then cut into bite-size pieces half the thickness of the block. Drain.

2.   Slice the champignons fine. Chop the scallion and cut the ginger root into thin slices. Briefly boil the peas in salted water.

3.   In a large frying pan—preferably a Chinese *wok*—heat salad oil. Sauté the scallion and ginger in the oil. Remove and discard. Reduce the heat to low. Add the stock and oyster sauce to the pan. Then add the tofu.

4.   Next add the champignons and season with soy sauce, sakè, and pepper. Simmer for a short while. Add green peas and finally stir in cornstarch dissoved in 2 Tbsp water. Cook till the mixture is thick and clear. Serve at once.

Serves four.

Butter-fried Tofu

2 blocks regular tofu
$\frac{1}{2}$ onion
$1\frac{1}{5}$ oz (40 g) butter
1 Tbsp minced parsley
julienne-sliced lemon rind
2 Tbsp grated Parmesan cheese
salt
monosodium glutamate

1.   Select firm tofu. Cut each block vertically in half and crosswise into slices $\frac{3}{4}$ in (2 cm) thick.

2.   Peel the onion and slice it into thin semicircular slices. Sprinkle them with salt, wrap them in a towel, and allow them to stand in running water long enough to remove their strong taste.

3.   Melt butter in a frying pan. Wipe the pieces of tofu with a towel. Brown them well on both sides in the hot butter.

4.   Serve the fried pieces sprinkled with sliced onion, minced parsley, lemon rind, and Parmesan cheese seasoned with salt and monosodium glutamate. Butter-fried tofu is delicious served with a dipping sauce made of soy sauce and mustard or of soy sauce and lemon juice.

Serves four.

Tofu in Peppery Pork Sauce (*Maabo-dōfu*)

This highly popular Chinese speciality is nutritious and inexpensive.

    1 block tofu
    1 4-in (10-cm) piece scallion
    1 small piece fresh ginger root
    1 clove garlic
    2 red peppers
    3 Tbsp salad oil
    7 oz (200 g) ground pork (or beef)
    1 heaping tsp Chinese miso or red miso
    2 Tbsp soy sauce
    1 heaping tsp sugar
    ¼ cup stock
    1 tsp cornstarch

1. Dip tofu in three cups boiling water. Remove. Cut into cubes ⅜ in (1 cm) to a side and drain in a colander.

2. Chop the scallion. Cut the ginger root into thin slices. Cut the garlic clove in half. Split the red peppers. Discard the seeds. Chop the peppers fine.

3. In a large frying pan—or Chinese *wok*—heat salad oil. In it sauté scallions, ginger, and garlic. When the oil is flavored with them, remove and discard these ingredients. Into the flavored oil put the chopped red peppers and ground meat. Stirring constantly, sauté these ingredients. When the meat is browned, add the miso, soy sauce, and sugar. Then add the stock and bring to a boil. Add the tofu and mix well.

4. Finally stir in cornstarch dissolved in 2 tsp water. Cook till the mixture is thick and clear. Serve at once.

Serves four.

Tofu Picatta

This is an interesting variation on the ordinary picatta dishes made with meat or shrimp.

    2 blocks tofu
    1 piece ginger root
    2 Tbsp soy sauce
    flour or cornstarch
    2 eggs
    ½ cup grated Parmesan cheese
    2 Tbsp salad oil

1. Drain the tofu in a colander. Cut it into bite-size pieces about ⅜ in (1 cm) thick. Grate the ginger and combine it with soy sauce. Marinate the tofu pieces in this mixture for a while.

2. Evenly coat the pieces of tofu with flour or cornstarch. Lightly beat the

eggs and combine them with the Parmesan cheese. Coat the pieces of tofu with this mixture.

    3.   Heat salad oil in a frying pan and, taking care not to burn them, fry the tofu pieces till golden brown.

    4.   Arrange on serving plates. Provide dishes of the ginger and soy-sauce dip. Or you may replace this dip with tomato ketchup, mayonnaise, lemon juice, grated *daikon* radish, mustard, a mixture of lemon juice and soy sauce, or the following sesame dip. Mix ½ Tbsp prepared oriental-style mustard, 1 tsp sweetened sakè (*mirin*), ¼ cup soy sauce, and 1 Tbsp ground, toasted sesame seeds.

Serves four.

Meat and Tofu Patties

    ½ block tofu
    7 oz (200 g) ground beef
    3 Tbsp minced onion
    ½ tsp minced ginger root
    1 tsp minced garlic
    2 Tbsp ground toasted sesame seeds
    1 tsp salt
    1 Tbsp soy sauce
    1 Tbsp sesame oil
    3½ oz (100 g) string beans

    1.   Wrap the tofu in a clean towel, weight it, and allow it to stand for thirty minutes. Without removing the towel, crush the tofu with both hands.

    2.   In a bowl combine the tofu, ground beef, onion, ginger, garlic, sesame seeds, salt, and soy sauce. Knead well with your hands. Then form into small patties.

    3.   Heat sesame oil in a frying pan and fry the patties till brown on both sides and done.

    4.   String the beans and boil them in two cups salted water. Do not overcook. Drain, cut into 2 in (5 cm) lengths, and sauté lightly in the pan in which the patties were cooked. Serve them with the patties accompanied with Worcestershire sauce, ketchup, or a mixture of soy sauce and prepared oriental-style mustard.

Serves four.

Tofu Omelet

    1 block tofu
    ¼ white onion
    2 stalks parsley
    2 Tbsp salad oil
    3½ oz (100 g) ground pork

1 tsp salt
1 tsp curry powder
1 Tbsp tomato ketchup
4 eggs
½ Tbsp butter
7 oz (200 g) boiled and buttered potatoes
1 tomato

1. Wrap the tofu in a clean towel and allow it to stand, lightly weighted, in a colander to remove water. Crush it fine.
2. Mince the onion and one stalk of parsley.
3. Heat 1½ Tbsp salad oil in a frying pan. Sauté the minced onion till translucent. Add ground pork and minced parsley. Continue sautéing till the meat changes color. Add tofu, salt, curry powder, and tomato ketchup. Stirring constantly, simmer till done. Remove from the pan and cool slightly.
4. Break the eggs in a bowl and combine them with the meat and tofu mixture.
5. Fry one-quarter of the mixture in omelet form. Repeat with the remaining ingredients to make a total of four omelets. Serve them garnished with boiled and buttered potatoes, tomato wedges, and parsley.

Serves four.

Tofu and Fish Patties (*Satsuma-agè*)

2 blocks tofu
18–21 oz (500–600 g) horse mackerel or sardine fillets pounded to a smooth paste
   in a mortar
1 Tbsp sugar
1 tsp salt
oil for frying
grated ginger root
combination of oriental-style mustard and soy sauce

1. Wrap the tofu in a clean cloth and allow it to stand weighted for thirty minutes.
2. Crush the tofu and mix it carefully with the smooth fish paste. Add sugar and salt and mix again thoroughly.
3. Wet you hands. Divide the mixture into four equal parts and shape each part into a fairly broad, oval patty.
4. Heat the oil to 340°F (170°C) and fry the patties in it till golden brown.
5. Serve with grated ginger root and a dip made by combining mustard and soy sauce.

Serves four.

Note: This dish is better if made from whole fish, skinned, cleaned, and filleted at home.

Deep-fried Tofu with Laver

> 1 block tofu
> flour
> 1 sheet dried laver (*nori*)
> oil for frying
> salt

1.   Wrap the tofu in a clean cloth and allow it to stand weighted for thirty minutes.
2.   Crush the tofu thoroughly in a mortar or food mill. Bind it with a little flour.
3.   Cut the *nori* into pieces about 2 in (5 cm) to a side.
4.   Put a spoonful of the tofu on the top of each sheet of *nori*
5.   Heat the oil to 340°F (170°C) and fry the tofu and *nori* in it till golden brown.
6.   Sprinkle with salt before serving. This dish can be dressed up by adding cooked green peas, chopped *shiitake* mushrooms, and chopped carrot to the tofu.

Serves four.

Deep-fried Tofu with Grated Radish (*Agè-dashi*)

> 2 blocks tofu
> 4 small eggplants
> 4 green peppers
> 2 Tbsp sweetened sakè (*mirin*)
> 2 Tbsp soy sauce
> 6 Tbsp stock
> oil for frying
> grated *daikon* radish
> grated ginger root

1.   Wrap the tofu in a clean towel and allow it to stand weighted for thirty minutes. Cut it lengthwise in half and crosswise in pieces ½ in (1½ cm) wide.
2.   Cut the eggplants into medium rounds and allow them to stand in cold water.
3.   Cut the green peppers in half lengthwise, remove the seeds, and wash the halves well.
4.   Prepare a dipping sauce by combining the *mirin*, soy sauce, and stock and bringing it to a boil in saucepan. Remove from the heat immediately.

5. In a deep frying pan heat oil to 340°F (170°C). Drain the eggplant slices and pat them dry with paper towels. Fry the tofu first. Then fry the eggplant and green peppers.

6. Arrange the fried foods on serving dishes with a mound of grated *daikon* radish, grated ginger root, and small container of dipping sauce.

Serves four.

Fried Tofu Balls

> **1 block tofu**
> **1 piece ginger root**
> **3 Jew's ears (*kikuragè*)**
> **7 oz (200 g) ground chicken**
> **1 egg yolk**
> **½ tsp salt**
> **sugar**
> **pepper**
> **oil for frying**
> **mixture of soy sauce and prepared oriental-style mustard to taste**
> **salt**
> **powdered *sanshō* pepper**

1. Wrap the tofu in a clean cloth and allow it to stand weighted for thirty minutes.

2. Mince the ginger and Jew's ears.

3. Pound the tofu to a smooth paste in a mortar. Add the chicken meat and mix thoroughly.

4. Add the egg yolk, ginger, Jew's ears, salt, sugar, and pepper. Blend well.

5. Wet your hands and form the mixture into small (1¾ in or 3 cm) balls.

6. Heat the oil to 340°F (170°C) and fry the balls in it till golden brown. Serve with a dip of mustard and soy sauce or with a blend of salt and powdered *sanshō* pepper.

Serves four.

Tofu and Cheese Fry

An excellent snack with beer or cocktails.

> **1 block regular tofu**
> **¼ lb (115 g) cheese**
> **flour**
> **oil for frying**
> **salt**

monosodium glutamate
tomato ketchup

1.   Wrap the tofu in a clean towel and allow it to stand weighted for thirty minutes.

2.   Cut the tofu lengthwise in half and crosswise into six equal pieces. Then divide the thickness of the resulting twelve pieces in half to make twenty-four pieces.

3.   Slice the cheese ⅛ in (5 mm) thick and cut it into pieces of the same areas as the tofu.

4.   Lightly coat the tofu in flour. Sandwich a piece of cheese between two pieces of floured tofu. Secure with toothpicks.

5.   Heat fresh oil to 360°F (180°C) and fry the tofu sandwiches till golden brown. Sprinkle them with salt and monosodium glutamate. Serve with ketchup. The tofu will not brown attractively unless fresh oil is used. Since the cheese will melt and run out, these tidbits must be fried quickly at high heat.

Serves four.

Fried Tofu with Mushroom (*Okabè-agè*)

Okabè is an old-fashioned imperial-court term for tofu.

½–1 block tofu
8–16 fresh *shiitake* mushrooms
cornstarch
prepared oriental-style mustard
soy sauce
1 egg
1 Tbsp water
3–4 Tbsp flour
oil for frying
grated *daikon* radish
salt
soy sauce
lemon juice

1.   Spread a clean towel on top of a chopping board. Place the tofu on the cloth. Wrap the edges of the cloth around the tofu and top it with another chopping board or a weighted plate. Allow it to stand for from thirty minutes to an hour. Then cut the tofu into pieces the same sizes as the caps of the *shiitake* mushrooms.

2.   Select mushrooms that are thick and unbroken. Remove and discard the stems. Wash and dry the caps and sprinkle the undersides with cornstarch.

3.   Coat the surfaces of the tofu pieces with prepared mustard and soy sauce.

Place a mushroom cap, under surface against the tofu, on the top and bottom of each piece. Secure with toothpicks.

4. Prepare a light batter by quickly combining beaten egg, water, and flour. Do not overbeat.

5. Heat oil in a frying pan to 340°F (170°C). Dip the tofu pieces in batter and fry them till golden brown.

6. Serve them with grated *daikon* radish, salt, soy sauce, and lemon juice.

Serves four.

Fried-tofu Salad

1 block tofu
dash of salt
oil for frying
½ cup cashew nuts
2 cucumbers
1 bunch radishes
¼ cup salad oil
¼ cup sesame oil
2 Tbsp vinegar
1 Tbsp sugar
1 Tbsp soy sauce
dash of salt
Chinese pepper oil (*ra-yu*)

1. Wrap the tofu in a clean, dry cloth and allow it to stand weighted for thirty minutes.

2. Cut the tofu into equal cubes and salt them lightly.

3. Heat oil in a frying pan to 360°F (180°C) and fry the tofu in it. Allow the oil to cool to 300°F (150°C) and fry the cashew nuts in it.

4. Cut the cucumber into thin rounds. Cut each radish into four equal wedges.

5. In a bowl combine salad oil, sesame oil, vinegar, sugar, soy sauce, salt, and pepper oil to make a dressing.

6. Heap fried tofu, cashew nuts, cucumbers, and radishes on salad plates and top with the dressing.

Serves four.

Yuzen Tofu

The name is a reference to the beautiful kimonos dyed in the *Yuzen* style in a city called Kanazawa. The colorful appearance of the dish is thought to suggest the bright colors of those garments.

2 blocks tofu
7 oz (200 g) white-flesh fish
$\frac{2}{3}$ oz (20 g) string beans
$1\frac{2}{5}$ oz (40 g) carrot
4 fresh *shiitake* mushrooms
1 piece ginger root
Seasoning A:
  2 Tbsp cornstarch
  2$\frac{1}{2}$ Tbsp sugar
  1 tsp salt
  1 tsp soy sauce
Seasoning B:
  $\frac{1}{2}$ cup stock
  2 tsp sugar
  dash of salt
Topping:
  1 cup stock
  1 Tbsp sweetened saké (*mirin*)
  $\frac{1}{5}$ tsp salt
  2 tsp soy sauce
  1$\frac{1}{2}$ tsp cornstarch

1. Bone the fish thoroughly and pound it to a paste in a mortar.
2. Dip the tofu briefly in five cups of boiling water. Drain, and squeeze, wrapped in a clean cloth. Combine the fish paste with seasoning A. Blend well and force through a sieve.
3. String and parboil the string beans. Cut them into diagonal slices.
4. Peel carrot. Remove and discard stems of *shiitake* mushrooms. Cut both into short julienne strips.
5. Combine seasoning B in a small saucepan. In this mixture simmer carrot and *shiitake* mushrooms till they are tender. Then add the string beans and cook for a few minutes before draining.
6. Combine these ingredients with the tofu mixture. Pour the resulting mixture into a rectangular mold and steam in a steamer for twenty minutes.
7. Combine all the topping ingredients except the cornstarch in a saucepan. Bring to a boil. Dissolve the cornstarch in 1 Tbsp water, add to the topping ingredients, and cook till the sauce is thick and clear.
8. Remove the steamed tofu from the mold, cut it into four equal pieces, and arrange these in individual serving dishes. Top each with the sauce and a small mound of grated ginger root.

Serves four.

Steamed Tofu with Shrimp

2 blocks tofu
8 shrimp
sakè
salt
cornstarch
4 pieces (3 in or 7 cm long) kelp for making stock (*dashi-kombu*)
8 fresh *shiitake* mushrooms
trefoil
mixture of equal parts of each of lemon juice, stock, and soy sauce
4 slices lemon

1. Cut each block of tofu in half crosswise. Spread a clean cloth in a colander. Place the tofu on top in a cloth-lined colander, salt it lightly, and allow it to stand for thirty minutes.
2. Shell and devein the shrimp. Sprinkle them with sakè, salt, and cornstarch.
3. Soften the kelp in two cups of water. Reserve the water.
4. Remove and discard the stems of the *shiitake* mushrooms. Wash the caps.
5. Spread a strip of kelp in the bottom of each of four wide-mouthed, heatproof serving bowls. Arrange equal portions of the tofu on top of the kelp. Place the shrimp and mushrooms beside the tofu. Pour some of the water in which the kelp was softened over these ingredients.
6. Bring water to a boil in the bottom of a steamer. Put the serving bowls in the top of the steamer and steam covered for six minutes.
7. In the last minute of steaming, sprinkle the ingredients in the bowls with chopped trefoil. Serve with small bowls of the lemon-juice and soy-sauce mixture and lemon slices

Serves four.

Tofu Sandwiches

1 block silken tofu
5 slices roast ham
green peas
1 Tbsp salad oil
2 Tbsp sakè
Sauce:
½ cup stock
salt
dash of pepper
½ tsp soy sauce
½ tsp sugar
cornstarch

1. Wrap the tofu in a clean, dry cloth and allow it to stand weighted for about thirty minutes. The traditional test for readiness is for the tofu to seem slightly softer to the touch than one's own earlobe.

2. Cut the tofu crosswise into slices ⅜ in (1 cm) thick.

3. Cut the ham into slices the same size as the tofu pieces. Parboil the green peas in salted water.

4. Heat salad oil in a frying pan. Fry the pieces of tofu till they are lightly colored on both sides.

5. Drain the tofu slices on paper towels. On a heatproof dish arrange—standing—slices of tofu alternated with slices of ham. Sprinkle the slices with sakè.

6. In the top of a steamer, steam the slices for from five to ten minutes.

7. In a saucepan combine all the sauce ingredients except the cornstarch. Bring to a boil. Add the juices from the dish in which the tofu and ham were steamed. Dissolve the cornstarch in 2 tsp of water and add to the sauce. Continue simmering until the sauce is thick and clear. Arrange the tofu sandwiches on serving plates and coat with the sauce. Sprinkle the top with green peas. If the ham is salty, adjust the seasoning of the sauce.

Serves four.

Shira-aè

> ⅓ block tofu
> ⅓ sheet devil's tongue jelly (*konnyaku*)
> 1 oz (30 g) carrot
> 2 dried *shiitake* mushrooms
> 1 pouch fried tofu (*abura-agè*)
> 1 Tbsp Jew's ears (*kikuragè*)
> 1 cup stock
> 2 tsp sugar
> 1 Tbsp soy sauce
> 3 Tbsp white sesame seeds
> 1 Tbsp light miso (preferably Kyoto miso)
> 2 Tbsp sugar
> ⅔ tsp salt

1. Briefly boil the tofu in two cups water. Drain wrapped in a clean cloth.

2. Briefly boil the devil's tongue jelly and cut it into slender rectangular strips. Peel the carrot and cut it into strips similar to those of devil's tongue jelly.

3. Soften the *shiitake* mushrooms in warm water. Discard the stems and julienne cut the caps. Dip the *abura-agè* in one cup of boiling water. Drain and julienne cut it. Soften the Jew's ears in warm water.

4. In a saucepan combine stock, 2 tsp sugar, and 1 Tbsp soy sauce. Bring to a boil, add the devil's tongue jelly, carrot, mushrooms, *abura-agè*, and Jew's ears. Simmer till well seasoned.

5.   Toast the sesame seeds. Pound them in a mortar. Add the tofu and continue blending. To this add gradually—blending with pestle all the while—the miso, 2 Tbsp sugar, and ⅔ tsp salt. Finish with a little of the sauce in which the ingredients in step 4 were simmered.

6.   Drain the ingredients cooked in step 4 and, immediately before serving, coat them thoroughly with the tofu sauce. Serve in deep individual bowls garnished with fresh leaves of the Japanese prickly ash (*kinomè*).

Serves four.

Tofu and Seaweed Salad

> **1 block tofu**
> **1 cup fresh *wakame* seaweed**
> *Sauce:*
> **1 Tbsp white sesame seeds**
> **juice of from ½ to 1 lemon**
> **1 tsp soy sauce**
> **1 tsp prepared oriental-style mustard**
> **pinch of salt**
> **½ cup salad oil**

1.   Drain the tofu.

2.   Allow the *wakame* to stand in freshwater to remove some of its saltiness. Wash it thoroughly and cut it into bite-size pieces.

3.   Toast the sesame seeds.

4.   In a bowl combine lemon juice, soy sauce, mustard, and salt. Beat with an egg beater while slowing adding the salad oil until a smooth dressing is produced. Finally add the sesame seeds.

5.   Cut the tofu in bite-size pieces. Combine it with the *wakame* in salad bowls and top with the dressing.

Serves four.

Salad of Tomatoes and Short-necked Clams

> **½ block silken tofu**
> **9 oz (250 g) fresh or canned shelled short-necked clams**
> **1 Tbsp sakè**
> **1 tomato**
> **5¼ oz (150 g) shallots**
> **parsley**
> **1½ Tbsp white sesame seeds**
> **2 Tbsp mayonnaise**
> **2 Tbsp vinegar**

      1 Tbsp sugar
      ½ tsp salt

    1.   Allow the tofu to stand for about thirty seconds in two cups of boiling water. Drain, wrap in a clean cloth, and allow to stand weighted for thirty minutes.

    2.   Wash the clams in salted water and drain them in a colander. Sauté them briefly in an unoiled pan. Sprinkle them with sakè.

    3.   Cut the tomato in half horizontally. Seed and dice it coarsely. Parboil the shallots in two cups boiling water. Squeeze them to remove slime. Cut into pieces 1¾–1½ in (3–4 cm) long. Mince the parsley.

    4.   Toast the sesame seeds and crush them to a paste in a mortar. Force the tofu through a sieve. Add it to the seeds in the mortar. Blend well. Add mayonnaise, vinegar, sugar, and salt.

    5.   Combine clams, tomato, and shallots and coat well with the tofu sauce.

Serves four.

Soy Sauce and Tofu Salad

      2 blocks tofu
      2 cucumbers
      4 slices roast ham
    Dip:
      1 Tbsp vinegar
      2 Tbsp soy sauce
      1 tsp sugar
      2 tsp sesame oil
      1 tsp ginger juice
      monosodium glutamate

    1.   Dip tofu briefly in five cups boiling water. Remove and plunge into cold water. Chill.

    2.   Plunge cucumbers briefly into boiling water. Immediately plunge into cold water. Cut into thin julienne strips.

    3.   Julienne cut the ham slices.

    4.   Drain the tofu and cut lengthwise in slices ⅛ in (½ cm) thick.

    5.   Arrange the tofu in the center of a large, flat serving dish. Mound cucumber on one side and ham on the other.

    6.   Make the dip by combining the ingredients listed. Serve in individual cups. This dish can be enriched by the addition of any number of other ingredients: bean sprouts, julienne-cut thin omelet, shrimp, Jew's ear, *wakame* seaweed, and so on.

Serves four.

Beef, Bean-sprout, and Tofu Salad

    2 blocks tofu
    1¾ oz (50 g) thin sliced, lean beef
    2 Tbsp sesame oil
    1 piece ginger root
    1 bud garlic
    1 piece (4 in or 10 cm long) scallion
    2 Tbsp toasted white sesame seeds
    dash of powdered red pepper
    7 oz (200 g) bean sprouts
    pinch of salt
    1 tsp sugar
    4 Tbsp soy sauce

1.   Dip tofu in three cups boiling water. Drain. Cut into fairly large cubes.
2.   Pound the beef slices, sprinkle them with sesame oil, and allow to stand a while.
3.   Mince the ginger, garlic, and scallion. Chop the sesame seeds.
4.   Mix garlic, ginger, scallion, and red pepper. Coat the beef slices in this mixture.
5.   Remove the hairlike roots from the bean sprouts and parboil them very briefly in three cups boiling water. Drain and salt lightly.
6.   Sauté the beef slices in an unoiled, heated frying pan. Sprinkle with sugar and soy sauce and combine with bean sprouts.
7.   Arrange cubes of tofu in individual dishes and top with the bean-sprout and beef mixture.

Serves four.

Pressed Tofu with Peanuts

    3 blocks tofu
    ½ cup shelled, unroasted peanuts
    oil for frying
    1 small green pepper
    1 Tbsp soy sauce
    1 tsp sesame oil
    ½ tsp mixed salt and *sanshō* pepper powder
    monosodium glutamate

1.   Wrap the tofu in a clean, dry cloth and allow it to stand, weighted on a tilted chopping board, for about thirty minutes.
2.   Dip the tofu into five cups boiling water then cut it into cubes about ⅜ in (1 cm) to a side.

3. Remove the thin inner coatings from the peanuts. Fry the nuts till golden in oil heated to 320°F (160°C).

4. Split the green pepper vertically in half. Seed it. Wash and then parboil it in one cup boiling water. Dice it.

5. In a bowl combine soy sauce, sesame oil, salt and *sanshō* pepper powder mixture, and monosodium glutamate. Blend well.

6. Combine tofu, green pepper, and peanuts and coat well with the sauce.

Serves four.

Note: If using salted peanuts, adjust the seasonings of the salt.

Fruit Salad

½ block regular tofu
juice of ½ lemon
3 Tbsp fresh cream
pinch of salt
pinch of pepper
pinch of sugar
1 orange
8 strawberries
1 apple
½ avocado
1 kiwi fruit

1. Roughly crush the tofu and force it through a sieve.
2. Blend the tofu well with lemon juice, cream, salt, pepper, and sugar.
3. Peel the orange and cut it into convenient pieces. Hull and wash the strawberries.
4. Peel the apple and avocado and cut them into convenient cubes. Peel the kiwi fruit and cut it into rounds.
5. Combine the fruits in a large bowl and top with tofu dressing. Canned fruits may be substituted for fresh ones.

Serves four.

Avocado Stuffed with Tofu

2 blocks tofu
2 avocados
¼ fresh pineapple
½ cup sour cream
2 Tbsp milk

1. Dip the tofu into three cups boiling water. Drain, wrap in a clean cloth, and allow to stand weighted for twenty minutes.
2. Cut the tofu into cubes ⅜ in (1 cm) to a side.
3. Cut the avocados in half and pit them.
4. Cut the pineapple into cubes ⅛ in (½ cm) to a side.
5. Blend sour cream and milk together.
6. Fill the avocados with pineapple and tofu cubes and top with sour-cream dressing. This tart, refreshing dish is very welcome in the morning. Canned fruits or fresh oranges and bananas may be combined with the tofu.

Serves four.

Tofu in Miso

> **tofu**
> **miso**
> **sakè**

1. Wrap the tofu in a clean, dry cloth. Allow it to stand weighted for thirty minutes. Wrap it in fresh, clean cheesecloth.
2. Thoroughly blend the miso and sakè. Add a little soy sauce for people who like piquant flavors or a little sweetened sakè (*mirin*) or sugar for those who like sweet foods.
3. In a suitable flat container, make a layer of the miso. On top of this, place the tofu, still wrapped in cheesecloth. Cover the tofu with a layer of miso. Smooth the upper surface. Allow this to stand overnight. Fish, meat, and vegetables may be lightly pickled in miso in the same way.

Yaki-dōfu (Toasted Tofu)

Homemade Toasted Tofu (*Yaki-dōfu*)

Follow the instructions for homemade tofu (p. 102), using 0.8 percent coagulating agent for a firmer texture. When the tofu is set, weight it lightly for about an hour to press out moisture. Then grill it over an open flame till both sides are lightly browned.

Sukiyaki-style *Yaki-dōfu* and Chicken Livers

> **1 block *yaki-dōfu* (or regular tofu)**
> **livers and gizzards from two chickens**
> **½ Tbsp sakè**

½ Tbsp soy sauce
1 package *shirataki* noodles (filaments of devil's-tongue jelly)
1 scallion
1 Tbsp salad oil
2–3 Tbsp sugar
2–3 Tbsp soy sauce
powdered red pepper

1. Cut the *yaki-dōfu* into dice ¾ in (2 cm) to a side.
2. Blanch the livers and gizzards well in cold water. Cut them into dice ¾ in (2 cm) to a side. Combine ½ Tbsp each of sakè and soy sauce and sprinkle this over the chopped livers and gizzards.
3. Parboil the *shirataki* in two cups boiling water then cut into convenient lengths.
4. Cut the scallion into diagonal slices.
5. Oil a sukiyaki pot or frying pan with salad oil. Lightly press moisture from livers and gizzards and sauté them in the oil. Add sugar and soy sauce.
6. Add *shirataki*, scallion, and *yaki-dōfu* in that order and simmer till the ingredients are hot and well flavored.
7. Sprinkle with red pepper before serving.

Serves four.

Yaki-dōfu and *Namari* Casserole

Namari is partly dried bonito. In this recipe, it is spiced with ginger to reduce the strong odor.

2 blocks *yaki-dōfu*
10½ oz (300 g) *namari* bonito
2 scallions
1 piece ginger root
2½ cups water
6 Tbsp soy sauce
2½ Tbsp sugar
1 Tbsp sakè
2 Tbsp sweetened sakè (*mirin*)

1. Cut the *yaki-dōfu* into slices ⅜ in (1 cm) thick.
2. Cut the *namari* into slices ¾ in (2 cm) thick. Briefly parboil it in two cups boiling water. Drain.
3. Cut the scallion into pieces 2–2¼ in (5–6 cm) long and grill the pieces briefly over an open flame. A wire-mesh grill facilitates this process.
4. Without peeling it, slice the ginger thin.
5. In a shallow pan combine water, soy sauce, sugar, sakè, and *mirin* and

bring to a boil. Add *namari* and ginger and bring to the boil again. Simmer for fifteen minutes over a low heat.

6.   Slide the *namari* to one side of the pan. Add the *yaki-dōfu* in the space left open and simmer for fifteen minutes longer. Add the scallion and simmer briefly.

Serves four.

Yaki-dōfu Simmered with Ginger

> 1 block *yaki-dōfu*
> 1 piece ginger root
> 1 cup stock
> 1 Tbsp sakè
> 2 Tbsp soy sauce
> 1 Tbsp sugar

1.   Cut the *yaki-dōfu* into bite-size pieces.
2.   Peel the ginger and slice it thin.
3.   Combine the stock, sakè, soy sauce, and sugar in a saucepan. Heat and ignite. Add the *yaki-dōfu* and ginger and simmer over a low heat for a while.
4.   Arrange the *yaki-dōfu* in a deep serving bowl and top with the pan juices. Take care not to use too much sugar, or the distinctive flavor of the ginger will be obliterated.

Serves four.

Yaki-dōfu and Chicken *Dengaku*

> 1 block *yaki-dōfu*
> 7 oz (200 g) boned chicken wing or breast meat
> salt
> sakè
> 1 block *konnyaku* (devil's tongue jelly)
> 8 taros
> miso sauce
> 4 in (10 cm) kelp (*kombu*)

1.   Cut *yaki-dōfu* into two-bite pieces and skewer on bamboo skewers.
2.   Slice chicken meat into bite-size pieces. Sprinkle with salt and sakè, and allow to stand for twenty minutes. Parboil briefly.
3.   Cut the *konnyaku* in bite-size pieces. Boil briefly and skewer.
4.   Peel taros. Boil till tender in salted water. Drain, wrap in a kitchen towel, and press to adjust them into as nearly perfectly round shapes as possible. Skewer.
5.   Prepare miso sauce according to directions on p. 112.

6.   Spread the strip of kelp in the bottom of a large casserole. Fill the casserole about half full with water. Bring to a boil. Add the *yaki-dōfu* and the *konnyaku* and simmer gently till heated through.

7.   Arrange skewers of *yaki-dōfu*, *konnyaku*, chicken meat, and taros on a large serving plate. Accompany with the miso sauce in a separate dish. Diners coat the skewered foods with the sauce according to their taste.

Ordinarily the dish called *dengaku* is prepared with regular tofu, but toasted tofu or *yaki-dōfu* has been firmed in the toasting process, does not crumble readily, and is therefore easier to use in the home.

Serves four.

Okinawa-style *Yaki-dōfu*

> 2 blocks *yaki-dōfu*
> salt
> 2½ Tbsp salad oil
> few stalks flat chives (*nira*)
> 10½ oz (300 g) bean sprouts
> 1¼ tsp salt
> 1 tsp soy sauce
> monosodium glutamate

1.   Salt the *yaki-dōfu*, wrap it in a kitchen towel, and press out moisture by allowing it to stand weighted for a while. A chopping board or a plate with a stone makes a suitable weighting device.

2.   In a frying pan heat salad oil to the smoking point. Crumble the *yaki-dōfu* into bite-size pieces and brown the pieces in the hot oil.

3.   Cut the *nira* into pieces 1½ in (4 cm) long. Add them and the washed bean sprouts to the frying pan and sauté rapidly over a high heat. Season with salt, soy sauce, and monosodium glutamate.

Serves four.

Yaki-dōfu Sautéed in Butter

> 1 block *yaki-dōfu*
> butter
> tomato ketchup or sesame-flavored miso

1.   Press the *yaki-dōfu* as in the preceding recipe to reduce its moisture content. Cut the block horizontally into two slices then cut each slice into bite-size pieces.

2.   Melt the butter in a frying pan and sauté the *yaki-dōfu* pieces on both sides.

3.   Serve at once with a garnish of tomato ketchup or miso flavored with toasted and ground sesame seeds.

Serves four.

Yaki-dōfu Topped with Grated Mountain Yam (*Yama-imo*)

> **2 blocks *yaki-dōfu***
> **1 piece 4 in (10 cm) long *kombu* kelp of the kind used in preparing stock**
> **2 cups stock**
> **1⅔ Tbsp light-colored soy sauce**
> **7 oz (200 g) mountain yams (*yama-imo*)**
> **powdered seaweed (*aonori*)**
> **vinegar**

1.   Cut each block of *yaki-dōfu* in half.
2.   Wipe the kelp with a wet cloth to remove grit. Spread the kelp in the bottom of a deep pot. Add the *yaki-dōfu*. Pour the stock over the *yaki-dōfu*. Cover with a weighted lid and bring to a boil. Reduce the heat to low and simmer for twenty minutes.
3.   Add the light-colored soy sauce and simmer for from five to ten minutes more.
4.   Peel the mountain yams and allow them to stand for ten minutes in vinegared water to prevent their turning black. Grate them fine. Add the remaining light-colored soy sauce to the grated yams.
5.   Arrange the *yaki-dōfu* in a deep serving bowl. Pour the grated yams over the *yaki-dōfu* and sprinkle with *aonori*.

Serves four.

Yaki-dōfu with Mushrooms and Walnuts

> **1 block *yaki-dōfu***
> **3 fresh *shiitake* mushrooms**
> **½ Tbsp salad oil**
> **1⅓ Tbsp soy sauce**
> **1⅓ Tbsp sakè**
> **1¾ oz (50 g) fresh English walnuts**

1.   Roughly crumble the *yaki-dōfu*.
2.   Clean the mushrooms. Remove and discard the stems. Julienne cut the caps. Sauté them in salad oil and flavor them with 1 tsp each of soy sauce and sakè.
3.   Pound the walnut meats in a mortar or grind them in a blender. Add the

yaki-dōfu and pound but not untill the *yaki-dōfu* entirely loses its shape. Season with 1 Tbsp each of soy sauce and sakè. Add the mushrooms and mix well. Serve in deep individual dishes.

Serves four.

Kori-dōfu (Dried-frozen Tofu)

Kōri-dōfu Mixed Casserole

     3 cakes *kōri-dōfu*
     3 cups stock
     4 Tbsp sugar
     1 scant tsp salt
     1 Tbsp light-colored soy sauce
     1 cup flaked dried bonito
     8 dried *shiitake* mushrooms
     1 cup stock
     $2\frac{1}{2}$ Tbsp sugar
     1 Tbsp soy sauce
     $3\frac{1}{2}$ oz (100 g) string beans
     $\frac{1}{2}$ cup stock
     2 tsp sugar
     $\frac{1}{2}$ tsp salt
     soy sauce

1.   Soften the *kōri-dōfu* in the following way. Put into a deep bowl. Pour over it boiling water to cover. Add a weighted lid to prevent the pieces from protruding above the surface of the water and allow to stand till soft and light.

2.   When *kōri-dōfu* is soft, holding each piece between the palms of the hands, gently squeeze out as much moisture as possible. Then let it stand in lukewarm water. Once again squeeze out moisture and soak in lukewarm water. Repeat these operations till the water running from the *kōri-dōfu* is clear.

3.   Pour three cups of stock into a large pot. Add the *kōri-dōfu*. Heat this gently. When the ingredients are warm, add 4 Tbsp sugar and a scant tsp of salt.

4.   After this mixture has simmered for ten minutes, add 1 Tbsp light-colored soy sauce. Add flaked dried bonito tied in a cheesecloth bag, cover with a weighted lid, and simmer over a low heat for fifteen minutes. Remove from the heat and allow to stand for a while to bring out the flavors.

5.   While the *kōri-dōfu* is cooking, soften the dried *shiitake* mushrooms in water, remove and discard the stems, and julienne cut the caps. Combine with one cup of stock in a small saucepan and simmer over a medium heat for from

twenty to thirty minutes. Add 2½ Tbsp sugar and 1 Tbsp soy sauce and simmer till all liquid has evaporated.

6. Again, while the *kōri-dōfu* is cooking, string the string beans, wash and salt them. Parboil them in one cup boiling water. Combine them with a half cup stock, 2 tsp sugar, and ½ tsp salt in a small saucepan and simmer briefly over a medium heat. In the last few minutes, add soy sauce to the pan. Drain the beans. Combine all ingredients in a large serving dish.

Serves four.

Egg-drop *Kōri-dōfu*

> 2 cakes *kōri-dōfu*
> 3 dried *shiitake* mushrooms
> 1½ in (4 cm) length carrot
> 2 eggs
> 1½ cups stock
> 1 Tbsp light-colored soy sauce
> 1 Tbsp sugar
> 1 Tbsp sweetened sakè (*mirin*)
> 1 Tbsp sakè
> ½ tsp salt

1. Soften the *kōri-dōfu* as explained in the preceding recipe.
2. Soften the *shiitake* mushrooms in lukewarm water. Remove and discard the stems and quarter the caps.
3. Peel the carrot and cut it into thin, rectangular slices.
4. Lightly beat the eggs with a pinch of salt.
5. In a shallow pan, combine light-colored soy sauce, sugar, *mirin*, sakè, salt, *kōri-dōfu*, and *shiitake* mushrooms. Bring to a boil, reduce heat to low, and simmer for about ten minutes.
6. Add carrots. When the carrots are tender, stirring constantly with a circular motion, slowly pour in the beaten eggs. When the eggs are half-set, remove the pan from the heat. Cover it with a lid and allow the eggs to set completely.

Serves four.

Grilled *Kōri-dōfu*

> 3 blocks *kōri-dōfu*
> 1¾ cups stock
> 5 Tbsp sugar
> 2 Tbsp sweetened sakè (*mirin*)
> 1 Tbsp soy sauce
> ½ tsp salt

salad oil
grated *daikon* radish
ginger root, scallions or chives

1. Soak the *kōri-dōfu* in lukewarm water to soften it.
2. In a saucepan combine stock, sugar, *mirin*, soy sauce, and salt. Bring to a boil. Add the *kōri-dōfu*. Cover with a lid that fits down into the pan to keep the *kōri-dōfu* submerged. Immediately before the liquid reaches the boiling point, lower the heat at once and simmer for twenty minutes.
3. Drain the *kōri-dōfu* and brush it with salad oil. Grill it over a low direct flame. Cut it into bite-size pieces.
4. Serve the *kōri-dōfu* with plenty of grated *daikon* radish, grated ginger root, and chopped scallion or chives.

Serves four.

Kōri-dōfu Topping (*Soboro*)

4–5 cakes *kōri-dōfu*
2 cups stock
1 Tbsp sugar
4 Tbsp light-colored soy sauce
2 Tbsp sweetened sakè (*mirin*)

1. Grate the *kōri-dōfu*.
2. Wash it in freshwater. Change the water, drain, and press out as much moisture as possible.
3. In a saucepan combine stock, sugar, soy sauce, and *mirin*. Add the grated *kōri-dōfu* and cook over a low heat for about thirty minutes, taking care that it does not scorch.

Serves four.

Note: This topping can be prepared in quantity and stored. It is extremely handy to use in combination with cooked, ground meat and vegetables on hot steamed rice as a light meal.

Kōri-dōfu and Vegetable Sauté

4 cakes *kōri-dōfu*
9 oz (250 g) thin-sliced pork
ginger-root juice
pinch of salt
3 dried *shiitake* mushrooms
1 small carrot

1 medium onion
1²⁄₅ oz (40 g) snow peas
3 Tbsp salad oil
⅓ tsp salt
1 Tbsp sakè
1 cup stock
1 tsp sugar
1 tsp soy sauce
1 Tbsp cornstarch

1.   Soften the *kōri-dōfu* in boiling water. Soak it briefly in lukewarm water and press out as much moisture as possible. Repeat this process several times. Cut the *kōri-dōfu* crosswise into thin (⅛ in or ½ cm), rectangular slices.

2.   Cut the pork into thin rectangles about ½ in (1½ cm) and sprinkle the pieces with ginger-root juice and salt.

3.   Soften the *shiitake* mushrooms in warm water. Remove and discard the stems. Cut the caps into three or four equal pieces.

4.   Peel the carrot. Cut it into thin rectangular slices similar to the *kōri-dōfu* slices and boil them in about two cups of water till barely tender.

5.   Cut the onion vertically in half then, with the cut side down, slice each half into half-moon pieces.

6.   String the snow peas and boil them in salted water till barely tender.

7.   Heat the salad oil in a *wok* or other large frying pan. Add, in this order, the pork, carrot, *shiitake* mushrooms, *kōri-dōfu*, onion, and snow peas. Sprinkle salt and sakè over them. Add stock, sugar, and soy sauce. Sauté till the meat is done and the other ingredients are well flavored. Add to the pan 1 Tbsp of cornstarch dissolved in 2 Tbsp water. Simmer till the sauce is thick and clear.

Serves four.

Kōri-dōfu Tempura

4 cakes *kōri-dōfu*
2 cups stock
4 Tbsp sweetened sakè (*mirin*)
3 Tbsp sugar
3 Tbsp sakè
3 Tbsp soy sauce
⅓ tsp salt
2 green peppers
oil for deep-fat frying
Batter:
1 cup flour
¾ cup water
1 egg

1. Soften *kōri-dōfu* (see p. 138).
2. In a saucepan combine stock, *mirin*, sugar, sakè, soy sauce, and salt. Add the *kōri-dōfu*, cover the pot, and simmer over a medium heat for from eight to ten minutes. Remove from heat and allow the *kōri-dōfu* to steep in the sauce to enhance flavor.
3. Combine the batter ingredients in a bowl and mix lightly.
4. Heat the oil to 340°F (170°C).
5. Drain and squeeze the *kōri-dōfu*. Cut it into bite-size pieces.
6. Cut the green peppers vertically into four equal pieces. Discard seeds.
7. Dip *kōri-dōfu* and green pepper in batter and fry them, only a few pieces at a time, till crisp. Drain on paper towels. Arrange on serving plates. Since the *kōri-dōfu* has been simmered in a richly flavored broth, there is no need for the usual tempura dipping sauce.

Serves four.

Hakata Fry

> 2 cakes *kōri-dōfu*
> 2 cups stock
> 1 Tbsp sugar
> ⅕ tsp salt
> 1 Tbsp soy sauce
> 3 oz (80 g) boned chicken-breast meat
> sakè
> soy sauce
> 2 Tbsp cornstarch
> 2 small eggplants
> grated fresh ginger root
> oil for deep-fat frying
> *Batter:*
> 2 Tbsp flour
> 2 Tbsp water
> 1 egg
> *Dipping Sauce:*
> 5 Tbsp stock
> 2 Tbsp soy sauce
> 1 Tbsp sweetened sakè (*mirin*)

1. Soften the *kōri-dōfu* in hot (190°F or 82°C) then soak in lukewarm water and drain several times until it no longer exudes a milky fluid.
2. In a saucepan combine stock, sugar, salt, and soy sauce. Add the *kōri-dōfu* and simmer gently till well flavored.
3. Slice the chicken-breast meat thin and sprinkle with sakè and soy sauce.

4.   Lightly press the *kōri-dōfu* to remove some moisture. Slice each piece horizontally in half and lightly dust the cut surface with cornstarch.

5.   Sandwich chicken meat between the slices of *kōri-dōfu*. Cut each sandwich into four equal pieces crosswise.

6.   Combine the batter ingredients in a bowl and mix them lightly.

7.   Clean but do not peel the eggplants. Cut each in half lengthwise. Make shallow, lengthwise incisions in the skin sides of the pieces.

8.   In a saucepan combine the dipping-sauce ingredients. Bring to a boil and divide among individual serving bowls.

9.   Heat oil for frying to 360°F (180°C). Fry the eggplant pieces till tender. Dip the *kōri-dōfu* sandwiches in batter and fry till crisp and golden. Arrange with mound of grated ginger root, and serve with dipping sauce.

Serves for.

Kōri-dōfu with Hijiki

> **1 cake *kōri-dōfu***
> **1 oz (30 g) *hijiki***
> **2 cups stock**
> **3 Tbsp sugar**
> **½ tsp salt**
> **2 Tbsp soy sauce**

1.   Soften *kōri-dōfu* (see p. 138).

2.   In a saucepan combine 1 cup stock, 1 Tbsp sugar, and ½ tsp salt. Add the *kōri-dōfu* and simmer over a medium heat till well flavored. Cut into bite-size pieces.

3.   Wash the *hijiki*, taking care to remove all foreign matter. Then allow them to soak in freshwater for from fifteen to thirty minutes to soften.

4.   Cut the *hijiki* into pieces 1¾ in (3 cm) long. In a saucepan combine them with 1 cup stock, and 2 Tbsp each of soy sauce and sugar. Over a medium heat, simmer till well seasoned. Cool.

5.   Drain the *hijiki*. Combine with the *kōri-dōfu* pieces, and serve.

Serves four.

Kōri-dōfu Salad

> **2 blocks *kōri-dōfu***
> **1½ cups stock**
> **4 Tbsp sugar**
> **1½ Tbsp sweetened sakè (*mirin*)**

2 tsp soy sauce
pinch of salt
3–4 fresh *shiitake* mushrooms
few stalks trefoil (*mitsuba*)
French dressing
soy sauce

1.   Soak the *kōri-dōfu* in lukewarm water till soft. In a saucepan combine stock, sugar, *mirin*, 2 tsp soy sauce, and salt. Simmer the *kōri-dōfu* in this mixture for twenty minutes. Drain and cut into thin rectangular slices.

2.   Remove and discard the stems of the mushrooms. Toast the caps briefly over an open flame; julienne cut them.

3.   Cut the trefoil into short (¾ in or 2 cm) pieces and parboil them briefly.

4.   Prepare French dressing and season it to taste with additional soy sauce.

5.   In a salad bowl, combine *kōri-dōfu*, trefoil, and mushrooms. Toss lightly with the dressing.

Serves four.

Kōri-dōfu in Sesame-seed Sauce

2 cakes *kōri-dōfu*
1½ cups stock
1 Tbsp sugar
⅔ tsp salt
½ tsp soy sauce
5 fresh *shiitake* mushrooms
pinch of salt
1¾ oz (50 g) trefoil
Sauce:
3 Tbsp white sesame seeds
1 Tbsp soy sauce
3 Tbsp stock
1 tsp sweetened sakè (*mirin*)

1.   Soften the *kōri-dōfu* (see p. 138).

2.   Squeeze as much moisture as possible from the softened *kōri-dōfu*. Combine it with stock, sugar, salt, and soy sauce in a saucepan and simmer over a medium heat till well flavored.

3.   Remove and discard the stems of the *shiitake* mushrooms. Lightly salt them. Toast them on both sides over an open flame. Julienne cut them.

4.   Parboil the trefoil very briefly. Plunge in cold water immediately then cut into pieces 1 in (3 cm) long.

5.   Toast the seasme seeds. Then grind them to a paste together with the

other sauce ingredients in a mortar, adding 1 Tbsp of the pan juice in which the *kōri-dofu* were simmered.

6.   Drain and squeeze the *kōri-dōfu*. Combine it with the mushrooms and trefoil and coat well with the seasme-seed sauce.

Serves four.

Nama-agè

Homemade *Nama-agè*

Prepare firm tofu (like that used in *yaki-dōfu*) according to the directions on p. 102. Wrap in a towel and allow to stand fairly heavily weighted—for instance, with two dinner plates—for an hour, or until the tofu is about two-thirds its original thickness. Heat oil for frying to 356°F (180°C). Fry the tofu, one piece at a time, in the oil till it is golden brown and crisp all over. Drain on paper towels.

Nama-agè Hot Pot

> 2 blocks *nama-agè*
> 10½ oz (300 g) thin-sliced beef
> 3½ oz (100 g) flat chives (*nira*)
> 2 scallions
> 1 packet *shirataki* noodles
> 4 large *shiitake* mushrooms
> boiled bamboo shoot
> 1 strip kelp (*kombu*)
> 5 cups water
> 3–4 Tbsp soy sauce
> 2 Tbsp sakè
> 1 tsp sweetened sakè (*mirin*)
> *Condiments:*
> grated *daikon* radish
> chopped scallion

1.   Cut each block of *nama-agè* into four triangular pieces.
2.   Cut the beef into bite-size pieces.
3.   Cut the chives into pieces 2¾–3 in (7–8 cm) long. Slice the scallion diagonally.
4.   Dip the *shirataki* noodles in boiling water. Drain and cut them into convenient lengths.

5.   Remove and discard the stems of the *shiitake* mushrooms and slice the caps in half. Cut the boiled bamboo shoot into bite-size pieces.

6.   Spread the strip of kelp in the bottom of a large ceramic casserole or metal pot and add water, soy sauce, sakè and *mirin*. Bring this to boil, preferably over a heating unit at the table.

7.   When the water comes to a boil, add the other ingredients. The beef should be cooked only briefly or it will toughen: it should still be slightly pink when eaten. Serve the *daikon* radish and chopped scallion as garnishes.

Serves four.

Braised *Nama-agè*

> 3 blocks *nama-agè*
> 3 cups stock
> 3 Tbsp sakè
> 2 Tbsp sugar
> $\frac{1}{2}$ cup soy sauce
> 8 *kinomè* leaves of the prickly ash

1.   Remove some of the oil from the *name-agè* by pouring over it about two cups of boiling water. Then cut each cake into six equal pieces.

2.   In a saucepan combine stock, sakè, sugar, and soy sauce. Bring to a boil. Add the *nama-agè* and simmer over a low heat for about twenty minutes.

3.   Arrange on serving dishes and garnish with *kinomè* leaves.

Serves four.

Note: To ensure full-bodied flavor, the simmering should be long and gentle.

Variation:
This simple dish can be made more filling for young appetites by hollowing the *nama-agè* and stuffing it with ground meat, carrot, or other vegetables before the simmering step.

Nama-agè and *Wakame* Braised in Miso

> 3 blocks *nama-agè*
> $1\frac{3}{4}$ oz (50 g) softened *wakame* seaweed
> 1 scallion
> 1 piece ginger root
> 2 cups stock
> $2\frac{4}{5}$ oz (80 g) miso
> $1\frac{1}{2}$ Tbsp sugar
> 1 Tbsp sakè

1. Remove some of the oil from the *nama-agè* by pouring over it about two cups of boiling water. Drain it well then cut each block into four equal pieces.

2. Squeeze moisture from the *wakame* seaweed and cut it into pieces about ¾ in (2 cm) long. Cut the scallion diagonally.

3. Peel the ginger root, cut it into fine julienne strips, and refresh it in cold water.

4. In a saucepan combine and bring to a boil the stock, miso, sugar, and sakè, then add the *nama-agè*. Cover the pan with a lid that fits down inside the pan to keep the *nama-agè* submerged. Simmer over a medium heat until the *nama-agè* is well flavored.

5. Add the *wakame* and scallion and simmer another three or four minutes. Arrange in serving dishes. Top each serving with julienne-cut ginger root.

Serves four.

Stuffed *Nama-agè*

> **2 blocks *nama-agè***
> **2 boned and skinned chicken breasts**
> **2 dried *shiitake* mushrooms**
> **⅔ oz (20 g) carrot**
> **⅓ scallion**
> **few stalks trefoil (*mitsuba*)**
> **1 egg**
> **1 tsp sugar**
> **1 tsp soy sauce**
> **1 ¼ cup stock**
> **2 Tbsp sweetened sakè (*mirin*)**
> **1 Tbsp sugar**
> **2 generous Tbsp soy sauce**
> *Sauce:*
> **⅘ cup stock**
> **2 Tbsp sweetened sakè (*mirin*)**
> **½ Tbsp sugar**
> **sakè**
> **soy sauce**
> **1 tsp cornstarch dissolved in 1 Tbsp water**

1. Remove some of the oil from the *nama-agè* by pouring hot water over it. Cut a deep pocket in the long side of each block.

2. Mince the chicken breasts fine.

3. Soften the *shiitake* mushrooms in lukewarm water. Remove and discard the stems. Julienne cut the caps. Peel and julienne cut the carrot.

4. Cut the scallion crosswise in thin slices. Briefly parboil the trefoil. Plunge it into cold water. Drain and cut into pieces ¾ in (2 cm) long.

5. Lightly beat the egg. Combine it with the chicken, mushrooms, carrot, and

scallion in a bowl. Season with sugar and soy sauce and mix well.

6. Stuff the *nama-agè* pouches with the chicken farce.

7. In a saucepan combine stock, *mirin*, 1 Tbsp sugar, and 2 Tbsp soy sauce. Add the stuffed *nama-agè* and bring to a boil. Skim off scum that forms on the water surface. Cover with a lid that fits into the pan so that the *nama-agè* pouches remain submerged and simmer for fifteen minutes.

8. In another saucepan combine stock, *mirin*, and sugar for the sauce. Season to taste with *sakè* and soy sauce. Bring to a boil. Add the cornstarch mixture and simmer till the sauce is clear and thickened. Sprinkle in the trefoil.

9. Cut each *nama-agè* in half, arrange the halves on a serving dish, and top with the sauce.

Serves four.

Grilled *Nama-agè*

> *nama-agè*
> grated ginger root
> grated *daikon* radish
> soy sauce

1. On a gridiron or wire net over an open flame, toast the *nama-agè* till the surfaces of both sides are crisp.

2. Cut into quarters and serve hot with grated ginger root, grated *daikon* radish, and soy sauce.

Fried *Nama-agè*

> 8 blocks *nama-agè*
> 2 scallions
> 2 Tbsp salad oil
> grated ginger root
> grated *daikon* radish
> *Condiment A:*
> more than 30 *kinomè* leaves (leaves of the prickly ash)
> 1 cup white miso
> ⅓ cup sugar
> ½ cup stock
> 1 egg yolk
> *Condiment B:*
> 2½ oz (70 g) red miso
> ½ Tbsp *sakè*
> 2 tsp sweetened *sakè* (*mirin*)
> 5 Tbsp sugar
> 2 Tbsp stock

1. Cut each block of *nama-agè* into two equal triangles and make a pocket in the cut side of each.

2. Slice the scallions into thin rounds.

3. Pound the *kinomè* leaves in a mortar. In a saucepan combine the white miso and all the other Condiment-A ingredients except the *kinomè* leaves and mix well. Stirring constantly with a wooden spoon over a low heat, cook till a smooth paste is formed. Add the *kinomè* leaves and remove from the heat.

4. In another saucepan combine all the Condiment-B ingredients and, stirring constantly, cook over a low heat till a smooth paste is formed.

5. Stuff the pockets of the *nama-agè* slices with sliced scallion. Heat salad oil in a frying pan and fry the *nama-agè* slices till golden brown, turning once.

6. Arrange on serving plates with small mounds of grated ginger root and grated *daikon* radish. Diners top the slices with the condiment of their choice.

Serves four.

Sweet-and-sour *Nama-agè*

> 2 blocks *nama-agè*
> 1 medium onion
> 2⅖ oz (80 g) boiled bamboo shoot
> 5¼ oz (150 g) carrot
> 2 green peppers
> 3 or 4 dried *shiitake* mushrooms
> 4 Tbsp salad oil
> 2 Tbsp sakè
> *Seasonings:*
> 1 Tbsp stock or the water in which the *shiitake* mushrooms were softened
> 1 Tbsp vinegar
> 1 Tbsp soy sauce
> 1 Tbsp sugar
> 1 Tbsp tomato ketchup
> 2 tsp cornstarch
> pinch of salt

1. Remove some of the oil from the *nama-agè* by pouring two cups of boiling water over them. Cut the blocks lengthwise in half and cut the halves into bite-size slices.

2. Cut the onion from the top into eight equal segments then shake the individual layers apart.

3. Cut the boiled bamboo shoot into bite-size pieces. Peel the carrot and cut it into bite-size pieces. Quarter and shell the green peppers and cut it into bite-size pieces. Parboil the carrot. Soften the *shiitake* mushrooms in lukewarm water. Remove and discard the stems.

4. Combine all the seasonings.

5. Heat 2 Tbsp salad oil in a *wok* or other large frying pan. Sauté the *nama-agè* pieces. Remove them.

6. Add remaining oil to the same pan. When it is hot, sauté the vegetables till nearly done. Add the *nama-agè* pieces. Pour the sakè into the pan, allowing it to flow down the sides. Add the mixture of seasonings all at once and, stirring constantly, cook till the sauce is clear and thickned. Serve immediately.

Serves four.

Nama-agè Sautéed with Green Soybeans

      1 block *nama-agè*
      7 oz (200 g) diced chicken meat
      1 Tbsp salad oil
      1 cup hulled fresh green soybeans
      1 Tbsp sugar
      2 Tbsp tomato ketchup
      2 Tbsp soy sauce

1. Remove some of the oil from the *nama-agè* slices by pouring over them a cup of boiling water. Cut each block lengthwise into four strips then cut the strips into bite-size cubes.

2. Put the chicken meat in a colander. Pour a cup of boiling water over it and allow it to drain.

3. Heat salad oil in a frying pan. Over a medium heat sauté the chicken meat. Add the *nama-agè*, soybeans, sugar, ketchup, and soy sauce. Reduce the heat to low and simmer till most of the liquid evaporates.

Serves four.

Note: Such other vegetables as green peas or green peppers may be substituted for the soybeans.

Nama-agè in Sesame Sauce

      1 block *nama-agè*
      carrot
      ***shiitake* mushrooms**
      1 cup stock
      ½ Tbsp sakè
      1 Tbsp soy sauce
      ½ Tbsp sugar
      3–4 Tbsp white sesame seeds
      1 Tbsp sugar
      ¼ tsp salt

1. Trim all the yellow outer skin from the *nama-agè*.
2. Julienne cut the *nama-agè* skin. In addition, julienne cut enough carrot and mushroom caps to equal the volume of *nama-agè* skin. Combine stock, ½ Tbsp sakè, 1 Tbsp soy sauce, and ½ Tbsp sugar in a saucepan. Bring to a boil. Add *nama-agè* skin, carrot, and mushrooms and simmer for fifteen minutes.
3. Toast sesame seeds in an unoiled pan. Pound in a mortar or grind in an electric blender. Add the white part of the *nama-agè* to the seeds and pound to a smooth paste. Season with sugar and salt to taste.
4. Drain the simmered *nama-agè* skin and vegetables well and coat them in the sesame-seed sauce.

Seves four.

Nama-agè in Barbecue Sauce

>*nama-agè*
>**bottled barbecue sauce**
>**salad oil**

1. Cut the *nama-agè* into bite-size pieces. Allow the pieces to marinate for a few moments in barbecue sauce.
2. Heat salad oil in a frying pan and sauté the *nama-agè* pieces on both sides. Serve hot.

Nama-agè with *Wasabi* Horseradish Sauce

>**1 block *nama-agè***
>**1 bunch trefoil**
>**1¾ oz (50 g) softened wakame seaweed**
>**small amount soy sauce**
>**1½ tsp prepared *wasabi***

1. Wipe the *nama-agè* and cut it into medium-size, rectangular pieces.
2. Plunge the trefoil briefly into a cup of boiling water. Dip it immediately into cold water. Squeeze out as much moisture as possible and cut into pieces 1 in (3 cm) long.
3. Cut the *wakame* seaweed into pieces ⅜ in (1 cm) long.
4. Combine the soy sauce and the prepared *wasabi* and blend well.
5. Combine the *nama-agè*, trefoil, *wakame* seaweed, and soy-sauce mixture in a bowl. Blend till the ingredients are covered with the sauce.
6. Serve in small individual dishes.

Serves four.

Note: Prepared mustard may be substituted for the prepared *wasabi* horseradish.

Abura-agè

Homemade *Abura-agè*

Prepare homemade tofu according to the directions on p. 102. Allow it to stand weighted for an hour to press out moisture. Then cut each block horizontally into slices ⅜ in (about 1 cm) thick. Heat frying oil to from 250° to 260°F (from 120° to 130°C). To prevent the oil's spattering, carefully dry each slice of tofu with paper towels. Slowly fry the slices till they have puffed well. Remove and drain them. Raise the heat of the oil to 390°F (200°C) and fry the tofu again till it is golden brown. This should not take long. Drain on paper towels.

Meat-stuffed *Abura-agè* in Broth

> 4 *abura-agè* pouches
> 1 slice bread
> 7 oz (200 g) ground pork
> ½ minced small onion
> 1⅖ oz (40 g) minced carrot
> 2 Tbsp minced scallion
> small amount minced ginger root
> ½ tsp salt
> 1 Tbsp sakè
> ⅓ oz (10 g) Jew's ear (*kikuragè*)
> 2⅘ oz (80 g) boiled bamboo shoot
> 3 cups broth
> 1 tsp salt
> 2 Tbsp sakè
> 1 Tbsp soy sauce
> ⅔ oz (20 g) snow peas

1. Cut each *abura-agè* pouch in half. Open the mouth of each half to form a small bag. Dip the *abura-agè* in boiling water. Drain.
2. Soak the bread in water. Squeeze out as much of the liquid as possible.
3. In a bowl, combine the pork, bread, onion, carrot, scallion, ginger, salt, and sakè and blend well by hand. Divide the mixture into eight equal portions.
4. Stuff the *abura-agè* bags with the meat mixture. Fold the tops of the bags over and place then, fold down, in a pan.
5. Soften the *kikuragè* in water. Slice the boiled bamboo shoot thin. Sprinkle these two ingredients over the *abura-agè* bags.
6. Combine broth, salt, sakè and soy sauce. Gently pour this into the pan. Cover with a lid that fits down into the pan and to rest on the *abura-agè* bags and simmer, over a medium heat, for twenty minutes.
7. String and parboil the snow peas.

8.   Arrange two *abura-agè* bags in each of four soup bowls. Pour soup and vegetables around them and garnish them with snow peas.

Serves four.

Noppei Soup

> 1 *abura-agè* pouch
> 1 small carrot
> 1 piece (4 in or 10 cm long) *daikon* radish
> 1 block *konnyaku* or devil's tongue jelly
> 5 or 6 taros
> 4 cups stock
> 1 tsp sakè
> 1½–2 tsp salt
> 1–2 Tbsp soy sauce
> small amount monosodium glutamate
> julienne-cut scallion

1.   Remove some of the oil from the *abura-agè* by pouring a cup of boiling water over it. Cut it into strips about ⅜ in (1 cm) wide.
2.   Peel the carrot and *daikon* radish and cut both into strips about the same size as those of *abura-agè*.
3.   Cut the *konnyaku* into similar pieces and boil them briefly in two cups of water. Drain.
4.   Peel the taros and slice them thin. Allow them to stand in cold water to remove astringency.
5.   Pour four cups of stock (preferably made from dried, flaked bonito, or *katsuobushi*). Add the *abura-agè*, vegetables, and *konnyaku*, and simmer over a low heat till tender.
6.   Season with sakè, salt, soy sauce, and monosodium glutamate and garnish with julienne-cut scallion.

Serves four.

Note: Small turnips may be substituted for the *daikon* radish, though quantities will have to be adjusted owing to the turnip's sweetness.

Abura-agè with Spinach and Sweet Potato

> 2 *abura-agè* pouches
> 2 cups stock
> 1 Tbsp sakè
> 1 Tbsp soy sauce

  pinch of salt
  1¾ oz (50 g) spinach
  1 sweet potato
  2 cups stock
  2 Tbsp sugar
  ⅓ tsp salt

1.   Remove some of the oil from the *abura-agè* by pouring a cup of boiling water over them. Cut them into strips ⅜ in (1 cm) wide.

2.   In a saucepan combine stock, sakè, soy sauce, and salt. Add *abura-agè* and simmer over a medium heat until the liquid is reduced to one-third its original volume.

3.   Thoroughly wash the spinach. Parboil briefly in three cups salted boiling water. Plunge into cold water at once and allow to soak a while to remove astringency.

4.   Remove the *abura-agè* from the saucepan, reserving the sauce. Put the spinach in the pan containing the reserved sauce and allow it to stand for a while, off the heat, to season.

5.   Wash but do not peel the sweet potato. Cut it into fairly thick rounds. Allow the slices to soak in cold water to remove astringency. In a saucepan combine stock, sugar, and salt. Add the sweet-potato slices and simmer till they are just tender.

6.   Combine the sweet potato, spinach, and *abura-agè* and arrange in individual serving dishes.

Serves four.

Chinese-cabbage *Shinoda* Rolls

  4 *abura-agè* pouches
  6 leaves Chinese cabbage
  1 small carrot
  1 strip (6 in or 15 cm long) kelp (*kombu*)
  1 strip (40 in or 1 m long) *kampyō* gourd
  2 Tbsp sakè
  1 Tbsp sugar
  2 Tbsp soy sauce
  pinch of salt
  citron (*yuzu*)

1.   Make a long sheet of each *abura-agè* pouch by cutting along three closed sides. Remove some of their oil by pouring a cup of boiling water over them.

2.   Wash the Chinese-cabbage leaves well and simmer them in five cups boiling water till wilted.

3.   Cut the carrot into coarse julienne strips and simmer them till just tender in

two cups boiling water.

4. Put the kelp in a pot and cover it with water. Bring to a boil. Remove from the heat.

5. Soften the strip of *kampyō* gourd in water.

6. On a cutting board, spread one long strip of *abura-agè*. On top of it spread three Chinese-cabbage leaves, arranging the first with the hard base end of the leaf to your left and the next with it to your right. Spread another sheet of *abura-agè* on top of the leaves. Along the center of this strip make a row of three or four carrot sticks. Roll the ingredients and tie the roll in three or four places with strips of softened *kampyō* gourd.

7. Remove the kelp from the pot and combine sakè, sugar, and 1 Tbsp soy sauce with the stock. In this, simmer the rolls over a medium heat for five minutes. At this point add another Tbsp of soy sauce and a pinch of salt. Then simmer till the rolls are tender and well flavored.

8. While they are simmering, cut the kelp and citron (*yuzu*) rind in fine julienne strips.

9. When they are done, cut the rolls into bite-size lengths and garnish with julienne-cut kelp and citron rind.

Serves four.

Savory Grilled *Abura-agè*

> 4 *abura-agè* pouches
> 2 Tbsp soy sauce
> $\frac{1}{2}$ Tbsp sweetened sakè (*mirin*)
> dash of monosodium glutamate
> $5\frac{1}{4}$ oz (150 g) *daikon* radish
> ginger root

1. Combine soy sauce, *mirin*, and monosodium glutamate to make a sauce.

2. Brush both sides of each *abura-agè* pouch thoroughly with this sauce.

3. The grilling should be slow and careful to prevent scorching. Place a brick on each side of a gas burner. Put the grilling rack on the bricks and adjust the heat to medium. Slowly toast the *abura-agè* till golden brown on this grill.

4. Peel and grate both the *daikon* radish and the ginger root.

5. Cut each of the toasted pouches of *abura-agè* into four equal triangular pieces and serve at once, garnished with grated ginger and *daikon* radish.

Serves four.

Note: This homely dish relies on the flavor of the *abura-agè* for its effect; consequently, the *abura-agè* should be fresh and thick.

Sautéed *Abura-agè* and Bean Sprouts

4 *abura-agè* pouches
5¼ oz (150 g) thin-sliced pork
½ block devil's tongue jelly (*konnyaku*)
18 oz (500 g) bean sprouts
6 dried *shiitake* mushrooms
⅔ oz (20 g) snow peas
3 Tbsp salad oil
scant ⅓ cup soy sauce
3 Tbsp sugar

1.   Remove some of their oil by pouring two cups of boiling water over the *abura-agè* pouches. Cut each vertically in half. Then, starting at the narrow end, cut the halves into slender strips.
2.   Cut the pork into julienne strips.
3.   Divide the thickness of the cake of devil's tongue jelly into quarters. Then cut these sheets crosswise into thin strips. Parboil the devil's tongue jelly briefly then drain it.
4.   Remove the hairlike roots from the bean sprouts and allow them to soak in cold water.
5.   Soften the dried *shiitake* mushrooms in lukewarm water. Remove and discard the stems and cut the caps into thin julienne strips.
6.   String the snow pea pods, parboil them, plunge them into cold water, and cut them into thin julienne strips.
7.   In a *wok*, or other large frying pan, heat the salad oil. Sauté the pork first. Add the devil's tongue jelly, *abura-agè*, bean sprouts, and mushrooms in that order. Season with soy sauce and sugar and, finally, add the snow peas.

Serves four.

Sautéed *Abura-agè* and *Hijikı*

2 *abura-agè* pouches
1⅖ oz (40 g) *hijiki*
small piece carrot
2 Tbsp salad oil
½ cup water
4 Tbsp soy sauce
2 Tbsp sakè
½ Tbsp sugar
1 Tbsp white sesame seeds

1.   Remove some of their oil by simmering the *abura-agè* in two cups boiling water for two or three minutes. Cut them into thin strips.
2.   Thoroughly wash the *hijiki*, taking care to remove any sand that may

cling to the pieces. Allow them to soften by standing for about fifteen minutes in cold water. Drain, reserving ½ cup of the soaking water. Wash and drain again.

3. Peel the carrot and cut it into thin julienne strips.

4. Heat salad oil in a frying pan. Sauté the *hijiki*, *abura-agè*, and carrot, adding them in that order. Add water and the strained water in which the *hijiki* were soaked. Bring to a boil over a high heat then lower the heat and simmer for twenty minutes.

5. Add soy sauce, sakè, and sugar and simmer till the liquid evaporates completely.

6. Toast the sesame seeds in an unoiled frying pan.

7. Serve the *hijiki* mixture in individual serving dishes with a topping of toasted sesame seeds.

Serves four.

Abura-agè and Greens

> 2 *abura-agè* pouches
> 1 bunch fresh greens, preferably *komatsuna*, spinach or Chinese cabbage
> 2 Tbsp salad oil
> 3 Tbsp soy sauce
> 2 Tbsp sakè

1. Simmer the *abura-agè* in two cups boiling water for two or three minutes to remove some of their oil. Drain them and cut them into bite-size triangular pieces.

2. Wash the greens and cut them into pieces 1½–2 in (4–5 cm) long.

3. Heat oil in a frying pan. Begin by sautéing the stem ends of the greens over a high heat. (If using Chinese cabbage, trim off the heavy bases of the leaves to reduce cooking time.) Next add the leafy parts of the greens, *abura-agè*, soy sauce, and sakè, and continue sautéing for about two minutes. It is important to cook these ingredients quickly over a high heat.

Serves four.

Stuffed and Fried *Abura-agè*

> 4 *abura-agè* pouches
> 10½ oz (300 g) potatoes
> ¼ tsp salt
> 1 Tbsp butter
> ¼ onion
> 1 green pepper

> 1½ Tbsp salad oil
> 5¼ oz (150 g) ground pork
> ½ tsp salt
> 2 Tbsp tomato ketchup
> 1 Tbsp Worcestershire sauce
> 2 Tbsp flour
> oil for deep-fat frying
> more Worcestershire sauce as needed

1.   Remove some of their oil by dipping the *abura-agè* into a cup of boiling water. Cut each piece diagonally in half.

2.   Peel the potatoes. After allowing them to stand a while in cold water, boil them till tender. Drain. Season with salt and butter, and mash to a smooth purée.

3.   Mince the onion and green pepper.

4.   Heat salad oil in a frying pan. Sauté the pork till it changes color. Add onion and green pepper and continue cooking. When the vegetables are tender, season with salt, ketchup, and Worcestershire sauce. Combine this mixture with the mashed potatoes. Divide the resulting mixture into eight equal parts.

5.   Stuff the *abura-agè* pouches with the meat mixture. Seal the openings by folding them and fixing them in place with a little flour mixed with water.

6.   Heat oil for frying to 340°F (170°C) and fry the stuffed *abura-agè* till the cases are crisp. Drain and serve with additional Worcestershire sauce.

Serves four.

Vinegared *Abura-agè* with Mourtain Yam (*Yamaimo*)

> 1 *abura-agè* pouch
> ½ moutain yam (*yamaimo*)
> 1½ Tbsp vinegar
> 1 Tbsp soy sauce
> pinch of salt
> ½ Tbsp sugar

1.   Remove some of their oil by pouring a cup of boiling water over the *abura-agè*. Slice then crosswise into thin strips.

2.   Peel the *yamaimo* and cut it into slices about 1½ in (4 cm) thick. Next cut these slices into thin julienne strips. Allow them to stand in vinegared water for a while to remove astringency.

3.   In a bowl combine vinegar, soy sauce, salt, and sugar.

4.   Combine the *yamaimo* and *abura-agè* and dress them with the vinegar mixture. Sliced cucumbers or other green vegetables are an excellent addition to this refreshing dish.

Serves four.

Abura-agè with *Tororo* Topping

> 2 *abura-agè* pouches
> ½ mountain yam (*yamaimo*)
> 1 Tbsp vinegar
> 1 Tbsp soy sauce
> ½ Tbsp sugar
> small amount citron (*yuzu*) peel

1.   Over an open flame, toast the *abura-agè* till golden. Cut it into bite-size pieces.
2.   Peel the *yamaimo*, removing a generous thickness. Allow it to stand in plently of vinegared water to remove astringency. Then grate it fine.
3.   Combine vinegar, soy sauce, and sugar in a bowl.
4.   Put the toasted *abura-agè* in fairly deep individual serving bowls. Top it with grated *yamaimo*. Over this pour the vinegar mixture. Garnish each serving with minced citron peel.

Serves four.

Note: Grate the *yamaimo* immediately before serving time to prevent its discoloring.

Abura-agè with Vinegar and Sesame Seeds

> 2 *abura-agè* pouches
> ⅔ oz (20 g) carrot
> 7 oz (200 g) *daikon* radish
> 1 cucumber
> dash of salt
> *Sauce:*
> 2 Tbsp toasted and ground white sesame seeds
> 2 Tbsp vinegar
> 2½ Tbsp sugar
> 1 tsp soy sauce
> monosodium glutamate

1.   Remove some of their oil by pouring a cup of boiling water over the *abura-agè*. Dry them briefly over an open flame then cut them into thin strips.
2.   Wash and peel the carrot and *daikon* radish and cut them into julienne strips about 2–2¼ in (5–6 cm) long.
3.   Cut the cucumber into thick diagonal slices then julienne cut these lengthwise.
4.   Combine the vegetables, salt them, allow them to stand a while, then wash them in freshwater. Squeeze out as much moisture as possible.

5.   Combine the sauce ingredients in a bowl. Add the *abura-agè*, toss, and serve immediately.

Serves four.

Inari-zushi

>   8–10 *abura-agè* pouches
>   2 cups stock
>   2 Tbsp sugar
>   1 Tbsp sakè
>   5 Tbsp soy sauce
>   2 Tbsp sweetened sakè (*mirin*)
> *Sushi rice:*
>   3 cups rice
>   3 cups water
>   ½ cup vinegar
>   4 Tbsp sugar
>   1½ Tbsp salt

1.   Cut each *abura-agè* pouch in half to make two pockets. Pour two cups of boiling water over them to remove some of their oil. Taking care not to rip them, open the mouths of each pocket.

2.   In a saucepan combine the stock, sugar, sakè, soy sauce, and *mirin*. Add the *abura-agè* and, over a low heat, simmer till the liquid is reduced to one-third its original volume.

3.   Thoroughly wash the rice. Combine it with 3 cups of water and allow it to stand for thirty minutes in the heavy pot in which it will be cooked. Bring the water in the pot to a rapid boil over a high heat. Reduce the heat to low and steam the rice for twenty minutes. Allow it to stand covered for another fifteen minutes.

4.   In a small saucepan, combine vinegar, sugar, and salt. Bring to a boil and simmer till the sugar is completely dissolved.

5.   Turn the rice out into a large, wide-mouthed container—wooden tubs designed especially for the purpose are used in Japan. Make a well in the center of the rice and pour the vinegar mixture into it. With a paddle or a wooden spoon, in quick slicing motions, mix the seasonings and the rice thoroughly. Either fan the rice with a paper fan while mixing it or train an electric fan on it to produce the desired gloss and consistency.

6.   Stuff the seasoned *abura-agè* bags with the sushi rice.

Serves four.

Gammodoki

Homemade *Gammodoki*

It is said that a Buddhist priest who longed to eat the meat his religion declared taboo invented *gammodoki* as a substitute. Made of tofu with additions of carrot, Jew's ear, *hijiki*, and—sometimes—gingko nuts, *gammodoki* are round and flattish patties. In Kyoto they are round and are called *hiryōzu*. In gredients and preparation method are the same for both.

> **2 blocks tofu**
> **2 oz (60 g) *yamaimo***
> **1¾ oz (50 g) carrot**
> **6 Jew's ears (*kikuragè*) softened in water**
> **2 Tbsp flour**
> **½ tsp salt**
> **oil for deep frying**

1. Drain the tofu weighted on a chopping board.
2. Grate the *yamaimo* and julienne cut the carrot and Jew's ear into short strips.
3. Pound the tofu in a mortar till smooth. Add the flour, salt, and *yamaimo* and mix till a smooth paste is formed. Add the well-drained Jew's ear and carrot. Divide the mixture into four equal parts.
4. Heat clean oil to a temperature of 338°F (170°C).
5. Oil the palms of your hands and form the tofu mixture into a patty ⅜ in (1 cm) thick and lower into the oil. When its surfaces have set—and not before, as premature jostling can cause it to crumble—move the patty to the center of the pan. Prepare another and lower it into the oil. Continue with the remaining ingredients.
6. When the patties float to the surface of the oil, turn them over and continue frying for three or four minutes or until they are golden brown all over. Remove and drain on paper towels. Freshly fried *gammodoki* are delicious with soy sauce flavored with freshly grated ginger root or with tomato ketchup and mustard.

If the mixture does not form patties easily, spread it on an oiled, flat plate and cut it into the desired shape with a knife.

Makes four gammodoki.

Oden

 4 *gammodoki*
 4 *satsuma-agè*
 2 *chikuwa*
 18 oz (500 g) *daikon* radish
 8 taros
 1 block *konnyaku* (devil's tongue jelly)
 8 in (20 cm) kelp (*kombu*)
 1¼ cup shaved bonito flakes (*katsuobushi*) or small dried sardines (*niboshi*)
 6–7 cups water
 ½ cup soy sauce
 scant ½ cup sweetened sakè (*mirin*)
 1 tsp salt

1.   Remove some of their oil by submerging the *gammodoki* and *satsuma-agè* in boiling water briefly. Cut the *chikuwa* in convenient diagonal slices.
2.   Peel the *daikon* radish. Cut it into slices 2¼ in or 3 cm thick. Trim off the corners of the upper and lower surfaces of each slice. Parboil them.
3.   Peel the taros, rub them in salt to remove their slime, and rinse them in cold water.
4.   Parboil then quarter the *konnyaku*.
5.   Clean the kelp by wiping it with a damp cloth. Cut it crosswise into strips about 2 in (5 cm) wide. Soften the strips in water then tie each in a bow.
6.   Prepare stock with the water, kelp, and bonito flakes or sardines. Its flavor should be a little stronger than is usual for soups and other lighter dishes. Season the stock with soy sauce, *mirin*, and salt.
7.   Combine all the prepared ingredients in a large pot. Add enough stock barely to cover them. Bring to a boil over a high heat. Lower the heat to medium and simmer, covered for two or three hours, adding stock as necessary. Before serving, correct the seasoning.

Serves four.

Braised *Gammodoki*

 8 *gammodoki*
 1¾ cups stock
 1 Tbsp sakè
 2 Tbsp soy sauce
 1 Tbsp sugar
 dash of monosodium glutamate
 ⅕ cup grated *daikon* radish
 prepared mustard

1.   Remove some of their oil by pouring boiling water over the *gammodoki* then allowing them to drain in a colander.

2.   In a deep saucepan combine stock, sakè, soy sauce, sugar, and monosodium glutamate. Add *gammodoki* and bring to the boil.

3.   Cover with a lid that fits down into the pan to keep the *gammodoki* submerged and simmer gently over a low heat for twenty minutes.

4.   Heap the *gammodoki* in a serving bowl. Pour some of the simmering liquid over them and serve them with grated *daikon* radish and mustard as condiments.

Serves four.

Dutch-style Fried *Gammodoki*

> **enough paste for 12 *gammodoki***
> **3½ oz (100 g) ground pork**
> **oil for frying**
> **1¾ cups stock**
> **1 Tbsp sakè**
> **2 Tbsp soy sauce**
> **1 Tbsp sugar**
> **dash of monosodium glutamate**
> **4 hot green peppers**

1.   Prepare paste for homemade *gammodoki* according to the directions on p. 161.

2.   Add ground pork to the paste and blend thoroughly.

3.   Shape the paste into twelve small balls. Heat oil for frying and fry the balls till golden.

4.   Pour boiling water over the *gammodoki* to remove some of their oil and allow them to drain.

5.   In a saucepan combine stock, sakè, soy sauce, sugar, and monosodium glutamate. Bring to a boil then reduce heat and simmer for ten minutes.

6.   With the tip of a knife, make vertical cuts in the peppers. Grill them briefly over an open flame. Add them to the stock mixture.

7.   Serve the *gammodoki* with this sauce and the peppers.

Serves four.

Salmon-stuffed *Gammodoki*

> **enough paste for 8 to 12 *gammodoki***
> **1 small can of salmon**
> **few drops ginger juice (pressed from grated ginger root)**
> **1 tsp cornstarch (or starch made from the dogtooth violet)**
> **oil for deep-frying**
> **5¼ oz (150 g) spinach**
> **1¾ cups stock**
> **1 Tbsp sakè**

2 Tbsp soy sauce
1 Tbsp sugar
dash of monosodium glutamate
½ cup grated *daikon* radish
salt
lemon juice

1.   Prepare paste for homemade *gammodoki* according to instructions on p. 161. Blend well and shape into eight or twelve balls.
2.   Lightly drain canned salmon. Put it in a bowl, flake it with a fork, and combine it with ginger juice and cornstarch.
3.   With lightly oiled hands, flatten one of the balls. In the center of it put a portion of the salmon mixture, and wrap the *gammodoki* paste around to enclose the filling entirely.
4.   Heat oil to 360°F (180°C) and fry the *gammodoki* till golden brown.
5.   Boil the spinach till just tender. Squeeze out moisture and cut the spinach into pieces 1½–2 in (4–5 cm) long.
6.   Pour boiling water over the *gammodoki* and drain them.
7.   In a saucepan, combine stock, sakè, soy sauce, sugar, and monosodium glutamate. Bring to a boil. Add *gammodoki*, lower the heat, and simmer for fifteen minutes. In the last few minutes, add the spinach.
8.   Flavor the grated *daikon* radish with salt and drops of lemon juice.
9.   Arrange the *gammodoki* on a serving dish, surround them with sauce and spinach, and top each with a small mound of grated *daikon* radish.

Serves four.

Yuba (Soy-milk Film)

Simmered Fresh *Yuba*

4 (7 oz or 200 g) fresh *yuba* rolls
oil for deep-fat frying
1½ cups stock
2 Tbsp sugar
1 Tbsp sweetened sakè (*mirin*)
1 tsp salt
monosodium glutamate
spinach
soy sauce
julienne cut citron (*yuzu*) peel

1. Cut the fresh *yuba* rolls into pieces 1¾ in (3 cm) long.
2. Heat deep-fat frying oil to 340°F (170°C) and fry the *yuba* rolls in it till their surfaces are lightly colored.
3. Dip the rolls in hot water to remove some of the oil.
4. In a saucepan combine stock, sugar, *mirin*, salt, and monosodium glutamate and simmer till the sugar dissolves.
5. Add the *yuba* rolls and simmer for five minutes over a low heat. Remove from the heat and allow the rolls to steep in the sauce.
6. Briefly parboil the spinach. Plunge it in cold water. Squeeze out moisture and cut the spinach into pieces 1½–2 in (4–5 cm) long. In a saucepan, simmer the spinach briefly with a little soy sauce and monosoidum glutamate.
7. Heap the *yuba* rolls on a serving plate and garnish with the spinach and julienne strips of citron peel.

Serves four.

Stuffed *Yuba* Rolls

> 3 sheets *yuba*
> 2 cups bean sprouts
> 1 scallion
> 5¼ oz (150 g) ground chicken meat
> salt
> pepper
> oil for deep-fat frying
> flour
> *sanshō* powder

1. Put the dried sheets of *yuba* in flat-bottom pan. Pour lukewarm water over them and allow them to soften.
2. Thoroughly wash the bean sprouts and remove their hairlike roots. Wilt them in an unoiled frying pan.
3. Mince the scallion.
4. In a bowl, combine the chicken meat, scallion, and bean sprouts and season the mixture with salt and pepper.
5. Divide the chicken-and-vegetable mixture into three equal portions. Shape each portion into a cylinder the same length as the *yuba* sheets. Spread a sheet of *yuba* on a working surface. Sprinkle the flour over it. Put one of the chicken cylinders in the middle of the sheet and roll. Continue with the remaining ingredients.
6. Heat deep-fat frying oil to 340°F (170°C) and gently fry the rolls. Drain them on paper towels and, after cutting into convenient lengths, serve at once with salt, pepper, and *sanshō* powder.

Serves four.

Nattō

Miso Soup with *Nattō*

    1 pack (3½ oz or 100 g) *nattō*
    2–2½ oz (60–70 g) miso
    2½ cups stock
    taros
    scallions
    mushrooms
    carrot
    kōri-dōfu
    abura-agè
    trefoil (*mitsuba*)

1.   Pound the *nattō* to a smooth paste in a mortar. Add the miso and blend well. Add ⅘ cup stock and blend till smooth.

2.   The vegetables and other ingredients added to the soup may be varied to suit your personal taste and may be used in whatever amounts you like. Prepare them all and cut them into bite-size pieces. Wash the trefoil and cut it into short lengths.

3.   In a deep saucepan, bring 1¾ cups stock to a boil. Add the vegetables and ingredients of your choice except the trefoil and simmer them till tender.

4.   Add the *nattō* mixture. Bring to the simmer. Serve the soup in individual bowls with a sprinkling of cut trefoil.

Serves four or five.

Nattō Omelet

    1 pack (3½ oz or 100 g) *nattō*
    soy sauce
    8 eggs
    ¼ tsp salt
    pepper
    1 clove garlic
    1 potato
    2 fresh *shiitake* mushrooms
    1 green pepper
    1 tomato
    ½ medium onion
    2 scant Tbsp butter
    ½ tsp salt
    pepper

1. Sprinkle the *nattō* with soy sauce and mix.
2. In a large bowl, lightly beat the eggs and season them with ¼ tsp salt and pepper.
3. Mince the garlic. Julienne slice the potato, mushrooms, and green pepper. Peel the tomato and cut it and the onion into thin rounds.
4. Melt 1 Tbsp butter in a frying pan. Sauté the garlic and the potato till translucent. Add the other vegetables and sauté till done. Season with ½ tsp salt and pepper. Add the *nattō*, stir, and remove from the heat.
5. In a separate frying pan, over a medium heat, melt 1 Tbsp butter. Pour in one quarter of the egg mixture. Stir vigorously with a fork until the omelet begins to set. Put one quarter of the *nattō* mixture in the center of the omelet and fold one side over the other. Make four of these.

Serves four.

Nattō Burgers

> 1 pack (3½ oz or 100 g) *nattō*
> ½ medium onion
> 1 clove garlic
> ½ scallion
> 1 oz (30 g) carrot
> small amount softened *hijiki*
> salad oil
> salt
> soy sauce
> pepper
> ⅘ cup soy pulp (*okara*)
> ¼ cup flour

1. Mince the *nattō*.
2. Mince the onion, garlic, scallion, carrot, and *hijiki*. Sauté these ingredients in salad oil till tender and season them with salt, soy sauce, and pepper.
3. Add the soy pulp and continue cooking till it is heated through.
4. Turn these sautéed ingredients out in a bowl. Add the *nattō* and flour and blend well. Taste and correct the seasoning if necessary.
5. Form the mixture into patties and dust them with flour.
6. Heat salad oil in a frying pan. Brown the patties on both sides. Cover and cook over a low heat until done.
7. Serve them with tomato sauce or the condiment of your choice. Or coat them lightly in a mixture of soy sauce and grated ginger root or soy sauce and prepared mustard.

Serves four.

Nattō Sautéed with Bacon

> 1 pack (3 ½ oz or 100 g) *nattō*
> 3–4 slices bacon
> 4 in (10 cm) scallion
> small amount green peas
> sakè
> soy sauce

1. Cut the bacon into small pieces.
2. Cut the scallion crosswise into thin slices. Cook the green peas till tender if fresh or frozen. Canned peas may be used as they are.
3. Sauté the bacon. When it has rendered its fat, push the bacon to one side of the pan. Add the *nattō* and sauté in the bacon fat.
4. Season with sakè and soy sauce, add the scallion and green peas, and heat through.

Serves four.

Nattō Gammodoki

> ⅔ pack (2–2½ oz or 60–70 g) *nattō*
> 1 block regular tofu
> 1 tsp toasted black sesame seeds
> small amount grated ginger root
> oil for frying
> grated *daikon* radish,

1. Press moisture from the tofu by wrapping it in a clean kitchen cloth and allowing it to stand, weighted, in a colander for about two hours.
2. Pound the tofu in a mortar. Add *nattō*, black sesame seeds, and ginger. Blend well.
3. With lightly oiled hands, form the mixture into five patties.
4. Heat oil to 320°F (160°C) and fry the patties. Serve them with grated *daikon* radish.

Makes five gammodoki.

Nattō Fritters

> 2 packs (7 oz or 200 g) *nattō*
> 1 ¾ oz (50 g) carrot
> ½ scallion
> 1 ¾ oz (50 g) *chirimenjako*
> *nori* powder (*aonori*)

1 egg
½ cup flour
oil for frying
soy sauce mixed to taste with lemon juice

1. In a bowl, stir the *nattō* till it forms a fairly coherent mass.
2. Julienne cut the carrot. Slice the scallion thin crosswise.
3. Combine *nattō*, carrot, scallion, *chirimenjako*, *nori* powder, egg, and 2–3 Tbsp water. Sprinkle flour over the mixture and stir lightly.
4. Heat oil to 350°F (175°C). Drop the *nattō* mixture by spoonfuls into the hot oil and fry till crisp and golden. Drain on paper towels.
5. Serve with a sauce made by mixing lemon juice and soy sauce to taste.

Serves four.

Nattō and Spinach Appetizer

nattō
spinach
soy sauce

1. Mince *nattō*.
2. Briefly boil washed spinach in salted water. Plunge into cold water. Drain, squeeze out moisture, then mince.
3. Combine *nattō*, spinach, and soy sauce.

Miso

Miso Soup with Tofu and *Wakame* Seaweed

4 oz (110 g) red miso
⅓ block tofu
4½ oz (130 g) *wakame* seaweed
5 cups stock
sanshō powder

1. Cut the tofu into cubes about ⅜ in (1 cm) to a side.
2. Remove hard parts of *wakame* seaweed. Cut seaweed into convenient lengths and simmer in one cup stock till tender.
3. Pour four cups stock into a saucepan. Put the miso in a fine-mesh strainer. Submerge the strainer halfway and press the miso through it into the stock with the back of a tablespoon or a pestle. (In Japan, special strainers called *miso-goshi*

are available for this task.) Add the tofu and *wakame*. Bring to the simmer, skimming off all scum that forms on the surface.

4.   Pour into individual serving bowls and finish with a sprinkling of *sanshō* powder.

Serves four.

Miso and Oyster Hot Pot

> 5¼ oz (150 g) miso
> 3 Tbsp sweetened sakè (*mirin*)
> 10½–14 oz (300–400 g) large fresh oysters
> ½ cup grated *daikon* radish
> 1 bundle *shirataki*, the threadlike form of *konnyaku*
> 2 or 3 scallions
> 1 block tofu
> ½ large or 1 small carrot
> about 10 sprigs edible chrysanthemum leaves
> stock made from kelp (*kombu*)

1.   Combine miso and sweetened sakè and blend well. Paint a layer of this mixture over the bottom and lower walls of a large, heatproof, earthenware casserole that may be brought to the dining table.

2.   Combine oysters and grated *daikon* radish. Rub the oysters gently with the radish to clean them thoroughly. Discard the radish. Rinse the oysters in cold water then drain them in a colander.

3.   Parboil the *shirataki* then cut the strings in half.

4.   Slice the scallions on the diagonal into pieces about 2 in (6 cm) long. Cut the tofu into moderately small rectangular blocks. Peel the carrot. Slice it thin and then, using either a paring knife or a small cookie cutter, trim each slice into a floral shape. Remove and discard all but the tender edible chrysanthemum leaves.

5.   Combine all the ingredients except the chrysanthemum leaves in the casserole coated with the miso-*mirin* mixture. Add enough stock to fill the casserole. Bring to a boil then add the chrysanthemums. Using chopsticks, all the diners eat directly from the casserole.

Serves four.

Miso and Pork Stew

> 5¼ oz (150 g) miso
> 1½ carrot
> 1 burdock root (*gobō*)
> 1 block *konnyaku* (devil's tongue jelly)
> 2 potatoes

3 turnips
1 scallion
7 oz (200 g) thinly slice pork
1 Tbsp soy sauce
1 Tbsp sakè
shichimi **pepper powder or** *sanshō* **powder**

1. Peel the carrot and cut it into thin strips about 2 in (5 cm) long. Scrape the burdock root, cut it into strips about the same size as the carrot strips, and allow it to stand in cold water for fifteen minutes to reduce its astringency.

2. Boil the *konnyaku* for two or three minutes and slice it thin horizontally. Cut each thin slice into small squares.

3. Peel the potatoes, cut them in half, then slice the halves thin (⅜ in or 1 cm). Allow the slices to stand in cold water.

4. If the turnips have their leaves on them, cut them off, leaving about ¾–1¼ in (2–3 cm) of the stalks on the turnip tops. Peel the turnips and quarter then vertically. Cut the scallion into short lengths.

5. Combine the *konnyaku* and all the vegetables except the turnips and the scallion with six cups of water in a large pot. Bring to a boil then add the pork. Bring to the boil again, lower the heat, and skim off all scum that forms on the surface.

6. Add half the miso and the turnips. Simmer over a low heat for ten minutes.

7. Add the remaining miso, the soy sauce, and the sakè. Add the scallions and simmer a few minutes more.

8. Serve in individual bowls with a sprinkling of *shichimi* pepper powder or *sanshō* powder.

Serves four.

Toasted Miso

3½ oz (100 g) red miso
3½ oz (100 g) boned raw chicken meat
4 fresh *shiitake* **mushrooms**
1 small piece ginger root
3 hulled English walnuts
1 Tbsp salad oil
2 Tbsp sugar
3 Tbsp sakè

1. Cut the chicken meat into slender julienne strips.

2. Remove and discard the mushroom stems. Cut the caps into slender julienne strips. Peel the ginger root and cut it into slender julienne strips. Mince the walnuts.

3. Heat salad oil in a frying pan. Add the ginger and sauté till it is fragrant. Add the chicken and mushrooms and continue sautéing till the meat is done.

4. Add the miso, sugar, and sakè. Continue to cook till the sugar has melted and a paste has formed. Sprinkle the minced walnuts over the mixture.

5. Spread the mixture on the bottom of a shallow, heatproof dish. Invert the dish over an open flame and toast it till lightly browned and fragrant. Serve as an accompaniment for plain steamed rice.

Serves four.

Miso Seasoning Paste

1 cup sweet miso
4 Tbsp sweetened sakè (*mirin*)
½ cup sugar
1 cup stock

1. Combine miso, *mirin*, sugar, and stock in a saucepan. Over a low heat, blend well with a wooden spoon or a rubber spatula.

2. Stirring constantly, cook till the mixture is glossy and smooth. This step requires caution since the mixture scorches easily.

This paste is useful in a number of dishes and is capable of considerable variation. Simmered slices of *daikon* radish are delicious served hot topped it. It may be combined with vinegar to make *sumiso*, which is used to sauce sliced raw tuna and scallions or cooked pork and scallions as an appetizer to serve with sakè. Or it may be used as a coating for tofu, mushrooms, fish, and other ingredients that are then grilled over a charcoal fire. The basic paste may be dressed up with additions of toasted and ground sesame seeds or with grated lemon peel or, even better, the grated peel of the *yuzu* citron.

Miso Condiment (*Tekka* Miso)

1 cup red miso
3 Tbsp salad oil
½ cup sugar
sweetened sakè (*mirin*)
3 Tbsp toasted whole soybeans

1. Heat oil in a frying pan. Add miso, sugar, and *mirin* and, blending constantly, cook over a moderate heat.

2. When the mixture has become stiff, add well toasted soybeans.

The mixture may be enriched with julienne-cut sautéed burdock root or carrot. It is convenient to have on hand to serve with drinks, to use as a filling in *onigiri* rice balls for box lunches, or to eat as a condiment with hot steamed rice.

Soy Milk

Carrot Muffins

⅔ cup soy milk
7 oz (200 g) carrot
7 oz (200 g) all-purpose flour
2 tsp baking powder
2⅘ oz (80 g) butter
4 Tbsp sugar
1 egg
1 tsp cinnamon
½ tsp vanilla extract
4 Tbsp grated Parmesan cheese
4 Tbsp raisins

1. Preheat the oven to 360°F (180°C). Peel and grate the carrot.
2. Sift the flour and baking powder together.
3. In a large bowl, cream the butter and sugar.
4. Add the egg, soy milk, cinnamon, vanilla, and carrot, in that order.
5. Add the flour, cheese and raisins, and blend well.
6. Grease and lightly flour muffin tins. Fill each about two-thirds full with the batter. Bake in preheated oven for twenty minutes.

Makes eight muffins.

Soy-milk Custard

1 cup soy milk
2 eggs
1¾ oz (50 g) sugar
½ tsp vanilla extract
Caramel Sauce:
2 Tbsp sugar
1½ Tbsp water

1. Preheat the oven to 320°F (160°C). Heat the sugar and ½ Tbsp water over a moderate heat until the syrup caramelizes and turns golden brown.
2. Dissolve the caramel with the remaining 1 Tbsp of water and remove from the heat.
3. Line the bottoms of four custard cups with caramel syrup.
4. Combine eggs and sugar and mix well. Add vanilla. Gradually beat in soy milk.

5. Pour the egg-and-milk mixture into the custard cups.
6. Fill a shallow pan with warm water. Stand the custard cups in the water. Bake in the preheated oven for from thirty to forty minutes or until a knife inserted in the custard comes out clean.

Serves four.

Soy-milk Blancmange with Strawberry Sauce

1 ¼ cups soy milk
1 ½ Tbsp gelatin
6 Tbsp sugar
3 Tbsp cream
½ tsp almond extract
4 Tbsp strawberry jam
1 tsp dry white wine

1. In a small saucepan, soften the gelatin in 5 Tbsp water for twenty minutes. Add soy milk and sugar and, stirring constantly, cook over a low heat till the gelatin dissolves completely. Do not allow the mixture to boil.
2. Cool, stirring from time to time.
3. Lightly beat the cream. Stir in the almond extract and fold the cream into the soy-milk mixture. The almond extract cancels the distinctive odor of soy milk.
4. Rinse a two-cup mold in cold water. Do not dry it. Pour the blancmange mixture into the mold and refrigerate till set.
5. Make strawberry sauce by thinning the jam with white wine.
4. Unmold the blancmange on a serving dish and surround it with the sauce.

Serves four.

Soy Milk with Powdered Green Tea

soy milk
powdered green tea (*mattcha*)
sugar

The distinctive odor of soy milk may be disguised for those who find it objectionable with additions of powdered green tea (or brewed or instant coffee or cocoa) and sugar. Other pleasing beverages may be made by puréeing pineapple, strawberries, or other fruits in a blender and combining them with soy milk and sugar to taste.

Soy Milkshake

> 1 ½ cups soy milk
> 2 eggs
> 3 Tbsp sugar
> pinch of salt
> ⅔ tsp vanilla extract
> dash of ground nutmeg

1. Separate the egg yolks and whites.
2. Beat the whites till they are stiff but not dry. In another bowl, combine the yolks, sugar, salt, and vanilla extract, in that order. Add the soy milk and beat well with a rotary beater or wire whip. Fold the egg whites into the soy-milk mixture. Pour in tumblers and top with sprinklings of nutmeg.

Serves three.

Soybeans

Simmered Soybeans

> scant ½ cup (2½ oz or 70 g) soybeans
> 1 tsp salt
> 1 medium carrot
> ½ lotus root
> 1 stalk burdock
> 1 strip (4 in or 10 cm to a side) kelp (*kombu*)
> ½ block devil's tongue jelly (*konnyaku*)
> 5 Tbsp sugar
> 5 Tbsp soy sauce

1. Allow the soybeans to soak overnight in 3½ cups water to which has been added 1 tsp salt.
2. Peel the carrot and the lotus root. Scrape the burdock. Cut all three into short, thin strips. Soak the burdock in water and the lotus root in acidulated water (water to which a small amount of vinegar has been added) to reduce their astringency.
3. Cut the kelp into pieces about ⅛ in (5 mm) to a side. Briefly parboil the *konnyaku* and cut it into strips similar to those in which the vegetables have been cut.
4. Bring the soybeans and their soaking water to a boil. Add 1¼ cups cold

water. Bring to a boil. Add another 1¼ cups cold water and bring to a boil again. Skim off scum that forms on the surface. Cover with a lid that fits down into the pan to keep the beans submerged. Lower the heat and simmer till the beans are tender but have not split their skins.

5.   Add the burdock and carrot and simmer for ten minutes. Add the lotus root, *konnayaku*, and kelp and simmer for another twenty minutes.

6.   Add sugar and simmer a few minutes. Finally add soy sauce and simmer five minutes longer.

Serves four.

Miso Soup Enriched with Soybeans

⅘ cup (4½ oz or 130 g) soybeans
3 cups stock
2 oz (60 g) red miso
chopped scallion

1.   Soak the soybeans in water overnight. In ample freshwater, boil them till tender. Drain and either pound in a mortar or run through an electric blender till smooth.

2.   In a saucepan, combine the beans and stock. Heat and, before the boiling point is reached, add the red miso.

3.   Soak the chopped scallion in cold water. Drain.

4.   Pour the hot soup into individual bowls and top with a sprinkling of scallion. The scallion may be replaced or enhanced with trefoil or with julienne strips of *abura-agè* that have been dipped in boiling water and drained.

Serves four.

Soybean Fritters

⅓ cup soybeans
⅔ oz (20 g) trefoil (*mitsuba*)
7 oz (200 g) shrimp
salt
additional flour
oil for frying
Batter:
5 Tbsp flour
1 lightly beaten egg
scant ½ cup cold water
Sauce:
1 cup stock
¼ cup soy sauce
¼ cup sweetened sakè (*mirin*)

1.   Allow the soybeans to soak overnight in water. Simmer them in ample water till they are tender but have not split their skins.

2.   Cut the trefoil into 1½-in (4-cm) pieces.

3.   Shell and devein the shrimp. Salt them and allow them to stand for a few minutes. Drain. Immediately before frying, dredge them lightly in flour.

4.   Combine water, flour, and egg. Mix very briefly. Do not worry if lumps remain.

5.   Heat frying oil to 340° F (170° C) or until a drop of batter sinks into it, rises quickly to the top, and remains spinning about on the surface.

6.   Combine beans, trefoil, flour dredged shrimp, and batter. Drop by moderate spoonfuls into the hot oil and fry, a few at a time, till crisp and golden. Drain on paper towels and serve as quickly as possible with a dipping sauce made by combining and heating stock, soy sauce, and *mirin*.

Serves four.

Soybeans and Spinach

⅓ cup soybeans
10½ oz (300 g) spinach
3 Tbsp mayonnaise
soy sauce

1.   Allow the soybeans to soak in water overnight. Simmer in ample water till the beans are tender but have not split their skins.

2.   Wash the spinach. Boil it briefly. Drain, squeeze out as much moisture as possible, and cut into short lengths.

3.   Flavor the mayonnaise with a few drops of soy sauce. Combine the beans and spinach in individual serving bowls and top with mayonnaise.

Serves four.

Soybean Rice

scant ½ cup soybeans
salad oil
2½ cups rice
3 cups water
3 Tbsp sakè
1 tsp salt
2 tsp soy sauce
1 strip (4 in or 10 cm to a side) kelp (*kombu*)

1.   Wash the beans. Pick over them carefully, removing all damaged beans and extraneous matter. Heat salad oil in a frying pan and sauté the beans for about ten minutes.

2.   Wash the rice thoroughly. Drain it in a colander.

3.   Combine the rice, soybeans, and water in a heavy kettle. Add sakè, salt, and soy sauce and spread the kelp on the surface of the water.

4.   Cover the pan with a tightly fitting lid. Bring to a boil over high heat. Remove the kelp. Lower heat and steam for twenty minutes. Remove from heat and allow the rice to stand, covered, for another fifteen minutes.

Serves four.

Bean Sprouts

Chicken Meatballs and Sobyean Sprouts

$3\frac{1}{2}$ oz (100 g) soybean sprouts
$\frac{1}{4}$ onion
7 oz (200 g) ground chicken meat
4 fresh *shiitake* mushrooms
$2\frac{1}{2}$ cups chicken stock or stock made with chicken bouillon cubes
juice squeezed from grated ginger root
soy sauce
salt

1.   Wash the sprouts.

2.   Mince the onion. Combine it with the chicken meat and mix thoroughly. Form into small meatballs. Simmer them in salted water for about fifteen minutes, or until done.

3.   Remove and discard the mushroom stems. Julienne cut the caps.

4.   Pour chicken stock in a moderately large saucepan. Add the chicken meatballs and the mushrooms. Simmer over a moderate heat for five minutes.

4.   Season with ginger juice, soy sauce, and salt. After a few minutes, add the soybean sprouts and simmer for an additional few minutes.

Serves four.

Sautéed Soybean Sprouts and Radishes

90 oz (250 g) soybean sprouts
3 red radishes

4 scallions
2 green peppers
1 Tbsp salad oil
2 Tbsp sherry
soy sauce

1.   Wash and parboil the sprouts. Wash the radishes and slice them thin. Slice the scallions thin crosswise. Seed the peppers and cut them into julienne strips.

2.   Heat the oil in a frying pan. Sauté the radish slices in the oil for one minute over a medium heat. Add, one by one, the bean sprouts, scallion, and green peppers. Sauté one minute longer.

3.   Add the sherry and, stirring constantly, cook for two or three more minutes. Season to taste with soy sauce.

Serves four.

Korean-style Bean-sprout Pickles

10½ oz (300 g) soybean sprouts
1 scallion
1 green pepper
garlic
ginger root
½ (or more) hot red chili pepper (or pepper oil to taste)
⅓ oz (10 g) dried shrimp
⅓ tsp salt
1½ Tbsp soy sauce
1 tsp vinegar

1.   Wash and parboil the bean sprouts. Plunge into cold water at once then drain well.

2.   Slice the scallion thin crosswise. Julienne cut the green pepper. Mince the garlic, ginger and chili pepper.

3.   Soften the dried shrimp by pouring boiling water over them.

4.   Combine salt, soy sauce, and vinegar. Marinate the other ingredients in this mixture, lightly weighted, for about two hours. The pickles will then be ready to eat.

Afterword

The remark that discovering a new, delicious food is more important than the discovery of a heretofore unknown planet made by the French gourmet Anthelme Brillat-Savarin (1755–1826) is well known. Certainly good food makes life richer, and good food that is highly nutritious too is a wonderful thing.

Soybeans and tofu, which meet both these requirements, were introduced into Japan many centuries ago from the Asian mainland. There are various versions of the route by which they came into the country. Some claim that Buddhist priests brought them in, while others insist that they were brought in by Korean prisoners of war. The ways of preparing and eating these foods too were at first either Chinese or Korean; but, with time, the Japanese people adapted them to suit their own tastes and preferences. The process of developing new, more delicious treats from soybeans products started long ago and continues today. For instance, housewives now take pride and pleasure in offering their families tofu in salads or in steak form.

Actually, because of the similarity between it and cheeses, tofu should be less puzzling to the modern Westerner than it probably was to the Japanese of those ancient times when it was first imported. Tofu is called bean curd in English. Curds are coagulated protein. In the case of cheese, the action of the enzyme rennet or of the lactic bacillus results in the phosphoprotein casein. (Lemon juice added to milk has a similar effect). In the case of tofu, *nigari* or calcium sulfate is added to soy milk to cause the coagulation of protein into curds, which are then transferred to box forms and allowed to set.

Though one is animal and the other vegetable, both cheese and tofu are produced in similar ways and have similar nutritional effects. We Japanese have grown accustomed to purchasing tofu in rectangular blocks. But, a decade ago, when I first visited China, I was astonished to see a tofu merchant wheeling a wooden wheelbarrow in which he had a large (about forty centimeters in diameter) round cake of tofu from which he cut the amount each customer required. I was immediately struck with the resemblance between his large round cake of tofu and the large round cakes of Edam cheese made in Holland. Tofu does not keep well but, processed into such foods as *sufu*, can be stored for a long time. Soft cheeses too spoil readily, though hard ones like Edam remain sound and edible for a considerable while.

Whether cheese was invented first and the idea of curds production exported along the Silk Road to China or whether Europe borrowed this idea from the Chinese custom of making tofu is now a matter confined to the realm of speculation. But it makes no matter, since both are part of the general store of worldwide human wisdom.

Why not start now taking advantage of the oriental way of using curds in a food that in many respects resembles the cheeses with which you are already familiar? Serve tofu cold or heated in warm water and with soy sauce—tofu itself contains nothing to give it a salty taste—and with traditional chopped scallions, red pepper, oriental mustard, or dried-bonito flakes or with whatever you have on hand in the kitchen, including prepared mustard, ketchup, or seafood cocktail sauce. Next you might use it in some of the ways in which cream cheese is employed: in dips, sandwiches, and sweetened in puddings and cakes. Crumbled, it can be used as a replacement for ground meat in hamburger patties, in meatballs, in gratin dishes, and in pizza sauce. Soybeans too may be boiled and mashed and used in many of these same dishes. No limitations can be set on ways to make good things to eat, and versatile soy products offer ample opportunity for creativity. I shall be very grateful if this book helps you accept the challenge of what may be a completely unfamiliar food to improve and enrich the way you and your family eat.

ASAKO KISHI

Bibliography

Abe, A. and Tsuji, S. *Book of Tofu*. Tokyo: Shibata Shoten, 1974.

American Soybean Association. *Soybean Blue Book*. 1983.

Food Research Institute. *Technology of Soybean Processing*. Extension Series of Food Technology, No. 4, 1966.

———. *Food, Its Science and Technology*. (Up-to-date technological topics concerning to soybean food.) Nos. 1–3, 5–12, 1958–69.

Ministry of Agriculture and Forestry. "Report on the present situation of *kori-tofu* industry." 1969.

———. "Agricultural statistics in Japan." 1983.

———. "Report on the present situation of *miso* industry." 1965.

———. "Report on the present situation of *shoyu* industry." 1965.

———. "Report on the present situation of *tofu* industry." 1969.

Shurtleff, W. and Aoyagi, A. *The Book of Miso*. Hayama, Japan: Autumn Press, 1977.

———. *The Book of Tempeh*. New York: Harper & Row, Publishers, Inc., 1978.

———. *The Book of Tofu*. Hayama, Japan: Autumn Press, 1975.

———. *Miso Production*. Lafayette, California: New-Age Foods, 1979.

———. *Tempeh Production*. Lafayette, California: New-Age Foods, 1979.

———. *Tofu and Soymilk Production*. Lafayette, California: New-Age Foods, 1979.

Smith, A. K. and Circle, S. J. *Soybeans: Chemistry and Technology*. Vol. 1, *Proteins*. Connecticut: AVI Publishing Co., Inc., 1972.

Umeda, I. "Modern shoyu production." *Journal of Japanese Society and Brewing*. Vol. 62, No. 1–Vol. 63, No. 4. 1967–68.

Umeda, I., Ebine, H. *et al. Fermented Foods*. Microbiological Industry Series. Tokyo: Kyoritsu Shuppan Co., Ltd., 1960.

U.S.–Japan Natural Resources Conference. "Proceeding of conference on mycotoxin." 1968.

Watanabe, T., Ebine, H. and Okada, H. "New protein food technologies in Japan." *New Protein Foods*. Edited by A. M. Altschul. Vol. IA. New York: Academic Press, 1974.

Watanabe, T., Ebine, H. and Ota, T. *Soybeans Foods*. Tokyo: Korin Co., 1970.

General Index

Index of Recipes